欢迎:中学汉

HUANYING

An Invitation to Chinese

WORKBOOK

JIAYING HOWARD AND LANTING XU

VOLUME 4

4
/
1

PART 1

Cheng & Tsui Company
Boston

Huanying Volume 4 Part 1 Workbook

Copyright © 2012 by Cheng & Tsui Company, Inc.

16 15 14 13 12 11   1 2 3 4 5 6 7 8 9 10

Published by
Cheng & Tsui Company, Inc.
25 West Street
Boston, MA 02111-1213 USA
Fax (617) 426-3669
www.cheng-tsui.com
"Bringing Asia to the World"™

ISBN 978-0-88727-711-5

Illustrations © by Murry R. Thomas, Landong Xu, Qiguang Xu, Lanting Xu, and Augustine Liu

Workbook design by Linda Robertson

Printed in the United States of America.

CONTENTS

OTHER RESOURCES

Audio Downloads

Throughout this workbook, you will see an audio CD icon to the left of many exercises. Audio CD icons indicate the presence of audio recordings, which are available as downloadable audio files. For information on how to download the audio files for this workbook, please see page iv of your *Huanying*, Volume 4 textbook.

TITLES OF RELATED INTEREST

Chinese Biographies
Graded Readers
By Grace Wu
Learn Chinese while reading the life stories of Chinese celebrities. Perfect for AP preparation.

Strive for a 5
AP* Chinese Practice Tests
By Weiman Xu, Han Qu, Sara Gu, So Mui Chang, Lisha Kang
Prepare for the AP exam with full-length practice tests, tips, and more.

Cheng & Tsui Chinese Measure Word Dictionary
A Chinese-English / English-Chinese Usage Guide
Compiled by Jiqing Fang, Michael Connelly
Speak and write polished Chinese using this must-have reference.

Visit **www.cheng-tsui.com** to view samples, place orders, and browse other language-learning materials.

第一单元 世界在变化

UNIT 1 The World Is Changing

 1.1 交通越来越方便了
Transportation Has Become More Convenient

一·听力练习

 I. 连连线! **Match Them!**

Match the phrases you hear in Audio Clip 1-1-1 with the definitions in Column B. Enter the corresponding numbers and phrases in Column A.

A栏： 请把你听到的写下来	B栏： 短语的意思
	rail transportation
	tourist group
	better and better
	in good spirits
	didn't get to go
	transportation is convenient
	travel by light rail
	a promise is a promise
	natural scenery
	travel by horse-drawn carriage
	to be affected
	five-day tour

II. 对话一理解 Dialogue 1 Comprehension

Listen to the recording of Dialogue 1 from Lesson 1.1 first, and then answer the True/False questions in Audio Clip 1-1-2.

	1	2	3	4
对				
错				

 III. 对话二理解 Dialogue 2 Comprehension

Listen to the recording of Dialogue 2 from Lesson 1.1 first, and then answer the True/False questions in Audio Clip 1-1-3.

	1	2	3	4	5
对					
错					

 IV. 回答问题 Answer the Questions

Answer the questions in this section based on your understanding of the Lesson 1.1 dialogues.

Directions: Listen carefully to the questions in Audio Clip 1-1-4 and record your answers on an audio recorder. You have 20 seconds to record your answers. If you do not have a recording device, arrange with your teacher to leave him/her a voicemail or write down your answers below in pinyin or characters.

1. _____

_____

_____

2. _____

_____

_____

3. _____

_____

_____

4. _____

_____

_____

5. _____

_____

_____

6. _____

_____

_____

V. 听对话 Listen to the Dialogues

Audio Clip 1-1-5 includes four short conversations. Each conversation is followed by a number of True/False questions based on its content. After listening to each dialogue, decide whether the statements below are true or false. Each dialogue will be played twice.

Dialogue 1	T/F
1. The last flight from Shanghai to Beijing leaves at 9:30 PM.	
2. There is a flight to Beijing every half hour.	
3. The longest flight from Shanghai to Beijing can take up to five hours.	
Dialogue 2	T/F
1. The man traveled by himself during the summer vacation.	
2. He toured the Yangtze River by boat for five days.	
3. He traveled by train for two days.	

Dialogue 3	T/F
1. Uncle Lin moved to Nanjing in the early 1980s.	
2. At first Uncle Lin came to Nanjing for work. But once he arrived in Nanjing, he decided to enroll at the university instead.	
Dialogue 4	T/F
1. Grandma Zhang went to Malaysia forty-eight years ago.	
2. She traveled by train and boat.	
3. She traveled for more than four weeks to get to Malaysia.	

 VI. 即时对话 A Simulated Conversation

Suppose you work for 世界漫游旅行社. Now you are talking to a customer, who is calling to inquire about tour packages to France and Italy. Read the travel flyer first. Listen carefully to the customer's questions in Audio Clip 1-1-6, and then answer them based on the information in the travel flyer below. After each question, you will have 20 seconds to record your answers. If you do not have a recording device, you can arrange with your teacher to leave him/her a voicemail. A vocabulary list has been included below the travel flyer.

法国、意大利七日游

发团社：世界漫游旅行社
价格：　成人：8860元/人，六岁以下儿童：7500元/人
出发地点：北京　　　　　　到达地点：法国巴黎
行程天数：7天　　　交通方式：飞机、火车、旅游汽车
出发日期：3月6日，3月18日，3月31日，4月6日，4月18日
电话咨询：020-1234567

每天餐饮：早、午、晚

交通工具：

 飞机

🚆 火车

🚌 旅游汽车

旅行日程：
第一天：北京 ✈ 法国首都巴黎
第二天：卢浮宫，埃菲尔铁塔，巴黎圣母院
第三天：巴黎百货商店购物
第四天：巴黎 🚆 尼斯，在尼斯海边散步休息
第五天：尼斯 🚆 米兰，参观米兰大教堂
第六天：米兰 🚆 威尼斯，参观圣马可广场教堂，坐贡多拉船游览
第七天：威尼斯 🚆 罗马，参观罗马城市，然后 ✈ 北京

Vocabulary

行程	xíngchéng	itinerary	咨询	zīxún	inquiry
巴黎	Bālí	Paris	卢浮宫	Lúfú gōng	Louvre Museum
埃菲尔铁塔	Āifēi'ěr tiětǎ	the Eiffel Tower	巴黎圣母院	Bālí Shèngmǔyuàn Notre Dame de Paris	
尼斯	Nísī	Nice	米兰	Mǐlán	Milan
威尼斯	Wēinísī	Venice	罗马	Luómǎ	Rome
圣马可	Shèngmǎkě	Saint Mark	贡多拉船	Gòngduōlā chuán gondola	

You may want to use the space provided below to jot down some notes or write down your answers in pinyin or characters.

1. _____

2. _____

3. _____

4. _____

5. _____

6. _____

VII. 中国文化短文 A Short Text on Chinese Culture

In Audio Clip 1-1-7 a student is giving a presentation based on a famous Chinese creation myth. After listening to the presentation, decide based on its content whether each statement is true or false. The presentation will be played twice. You can take notes while listening.

Below is a word bank that may help you understand the presentation better.

盘古	Pán Gǔ	proper name	挥	huī	wave
相信	xiāngxìn	believe	碎	suì	broken
宇宙	yǔzhòu	the universe	升	shēng	rise
混沌	hùndùn	chaos	浊	zhuó	muddy
睡醒	shuìxǐng	wake up	踩	cǎi	step on
周围	zhōuwéi	surroundings	永远	yǒngyuǎn	forever
举起	jǔqǐ	lift			

Notes:

对不对?

	对	错
1. Many Chinese people believe that in the beginning the universe was formless chaos within a shape like a large egg.		
2. Many Chinese people also believe that Pan Gu was the man who created the universe.		
3. In this legend, Pan Gu slept in the universe for 1,800 years.		

4. According to this Chinese legend, the blue sky is made of the clear and light elements of the universe.		
5. According to this legend, it took about 18,000 years for the sky to be separated from the earth.		

二·综合语言练习

┃. 汉语怎么说? **How do you say it in Chinese?**

If a word or a phrase is provided, try to use it in your sentence.

1. They have taken a 10-day tour of Europe.

   _____

2. Taking the train allowed me to see more natural scenery.

   _____

3. In the past, there was no highway. To get to the village one had to ride a horse-drawn cart.

   _____

4. Transportation has become more convenient and the world has become smaller.

   _____

5. We planned a trip to Italy. It was a pity that we couldn't go. (可惜)

   _____

6. It is a pity that you didn't take the light rail. Otherwise, you would have arrived here an hour earlier. (可惜)

   _____

7. Perhaps the flight time can be reduced by three hours. (大概)

   _____

8. Because rail transportation was affected by the weather, we had to wait in the railway station for 6 hours.

   _____

9. Since last April, he has been working as a tour guide. (从···以来)

_____

10. He has told me repeatedly that I can take the subway to the airport. (一再)

_____

II. 凯丽理解得对吗？ **Did Kelly understand correctly?**

The following is what Kelly said about how David and Tom spent their summer vacation. Based on Dialogue 1 in Lesson 1.1, decide whether Kelly's statements are correct.

	对	错
1. 暑假的时候，大卫和汤姆都去看爷爷奶奶了。		
2. 汤姆跟爷爷奶奶一起参加了一个旅行团。		
3. 大卫在爷爷奶奶家住了两个星期，然后去意大利玩了一个星期。		
4. 汤姆和大卫都是坐火车去旅行的。		
5. 汤姆和大卫都觉得坐火车比坐飞机有意思，因为可以看到很多自然景色。		
6. 汤姆很喜欢农村，可是大卫不喜欢。		
7. 汤姆参加的旅行团主要是参观中国东北的农村。		
8. 汤姆在中国农村旅游的时候，交通很不方便，只能坐马车。		
9. 因为马车走得慢，所以从一个村子到另一个村子，路上的时间比较长。		
10. 大卫觉得，因为交通越来越方便，世界变得越来越小了。		

III. 有什么不同？ **What's the difference between the two trips?**

Dialogue 2 in Lesson 1.1 describes two trips that Grandpa Lin took between Shanghai and San Francisco. Write down three differences between the two trips in the space provided below. After you have finished, compare notes with a partner.

林爷爷四十年代的旅行	林爷爷现在的旅行
1.	
2.	
3.	

IV. 结伴活动: 可惜！ **Pair Activity: What a pity!**

You and some of your friends have been planning a weekend trip to Hangzhou. However, after drawing up a plan, you and your partner have discovered that things aren't going as smoothly as you originally thought. Tell each other about the hiccups you are encountering and discuss how you will adjust your plans.

Share the problems that you discovered with your partner, following the example in Model 1. Be sure to use 可惜 in your conversation.

Model 1:　A: 今天下午两点我们一起去打网球吧。

B: 可惜我有事，今天不能跟你们一起去打了。

A: Give a suggestion (such as, 我们下个周末再去吧).

B: Respond to the suggestion (either accept it or make your own suggestion).

When your partner shares the problems s/he has discovered, take notes on your worksheet following the example in Model 2. Don't forget to include 可惜 in your notes. Discuss with your partner how to adjust your plan and write your decision in the column 我们的新计划.

Model 2:

我们原来的周末计划	我发现的问题	我们的新计划
玛丽娅跟我们一起去看电影。	Maria is sick and can't go to the movie with us anymore. 可惜玛丽娅病了，不能跟我们一起去看电影了。	我们可以下个周末去。

A's Worksheet

我们的周末计划	我知道的情况	新计划
1. 我们俩和小丽一起去杭州旅游。	Xiao Li has to go to a test-preparation class and can't go to Hangzhou with us anymore.	
2. 我们坐早上八点的动车去，下午六点的动车回来。		
3. 在杭州，我们可以去参观一个种茶的村子。	The village is under repair. There is not much to see.	
4. 我们可以去杭州的"楼外楼"菜馆吃午饭。		
5. 吃完午饭，我们去西湖坐船。	It will rain in the afternoon.	
6. 然后我们骑自行车去市中心。		

B's Worksheet

我们的周末计划	我知道的情况	新计划
1. 小丽跟我们一起去杭州旅游。		
2. 我们坐早上八点的动车去，下午六点的动车回来。	Tickets for the six o'clock train are all sold out.	
3. 在杭州，我们可以去参观一个种茶的村子。		
4. 我们可以去杭州的"楼外楼"菜馆吃午饭。	The restaurant will have a banquet at noon, so we may have to wait for an hour (大概).	
5. 吃完午饭，我们去西湖坐船。		
6. 然后我们骑自行车去市中心。	We can't ride bicycles downtown.	

V. 小组活动：大概原因 Group Activity: What's the most likely cause?

Step 1: Yesterday, some unusual events took place at your school. Form a group of three. Take turns guessing what the cause might be. Make sure that you use the word 大概 when making a guess. When your group members speak, take notes about their guesses.

Model: 昨天大概没有电，所以电脑都不能用了。

情况	我	同学一	同学二
1. 昨天学校电脑房的电脑都不能用了。	没有电		
2. 有人在学校看见两个不三不四的人。			
3. 昨天下午学校来了两个警察。			
4. 昨天校长看上去很不高兴。			
5. 有几个人在学校门口大喊大叫。			
6. 昨天看门师傅不见了。			

Step 2: Discuss your guesses in class. As a class, decide which ones are the best guesses.

VI. 小对话: 你一直在做什么? Mini-Dialogue: What have you been doing?

A	B
You start • Ask if B can go to a movie with you tonight. • Ask how long B has been volunteering there. • Apologize. Tell B you have to take a violin lesson tomorrow evening. • Tell B you have been taking violin lessons since last year (从···以来). Ask B if this Saturday will be a good time to go to a movie together. • Accept the appointment.	**Your partner starts** • Apologize. Tell A you have to volunteer at a senior center tonight. • Tell A you have been volunteering there since last March (从···以来). Ask A if you can go to the movie tomorrow evening. • Ask how long A has been taking violin lessons. • Tell A Saturday afternoon will work for you. Suggest a time and place to meet.
Your partner starts • Tell B you have been taking a college entrance exam preparation course since the first year of high school (从···以来). Ask if B has also been preparing for the college entrance exam. • Ask if B has heard about the website "Your Math Teacher." Tell B you have been going there since last year (从···以来). The website is helpful. • Ask B if you could borrow the book.	**You start** • Ask if A has been preparing for the college entrance exam. • Tell A you have been working with an English tutor since January (从···以来), and your English has improved. But you are having problems with math. • Thank A for the information. Ask if A knows about the book *Analysis of College Entrance Exam on Physics*. Tell A you have been reading it since last week (从···以来). It is very helpful. Ask if A would like to read it, too. • Tell A you will lend it to A as soon as you finish it.

VII. 哪家旅行社好？ Which travel agency has better services?

Your neighbor would like to take a group tour to China. He has found two travel agencies that organize China tours at similar prices. In order to make a good decision, he has collected several reviews about the two travel agencies, but all the reviews are written in Chinese. Your neighbor has printed out the reviews and asked you to help him make a decision. Read the comments carefully and write a one-sentence summary in the space provided.

游客的评论	一句话概括
四方旅行社☺☺☺☺☺ 我们全家参加了上海三日游。旅行日程安排得非常好。交通、食宿也都没有问题。我们特别喜欢四方旅行社的服务。每天早上，导游都把一天的活动告诉大家。如果有不清楚的地方，导游会很耐心地一再解释。下一次我们去海南岛旅行，也打算用四方旅行社。	
四方旅行社☺ 我和朋友参加了四方旅行社组织的南京一日游。我们车上有两个游客，他们到了一个景点就要拍很多照片，还要买东西。所以每次到了规定离开的时间，他们总是晚回来五到十分钟。一车的人都等他们。我们一再对导游说，"到了开车的时间就应该开车。"可是导游总是说，"再等几分钟吧。"所以我觉得，在我们的旅游中，很多时间都是在等人。	
四方旅行社☺☺☺ 四方旅行社的导游非常愿意为游客服务，可是导游必须知道，服务应该是为大家的，而不是为一个人的。我在上海旅行的时候，我们旅游团里有一位老先生要买不少东西。为了帮助他买东西，导游就带我们去了很多商店。多数的游客都不想买东西，可是也得去那些商店。虽然那位老先生想买的东西全买到了，可是这对多数游客来说，是不公平 (fair) 的。	

游客的评论	一句话概括
江山旅行社☺☺ 我参加了杭州两日游。导游很客气，交通、住宿也很好，可是我觉得在景点的时间太短了。每次到了一个景点，导游就说："给大家十分钟时间拍照，拍完照就上车，我们要去下一个景点。"我们没有时间好好参观，杭州两日游是"走马观花"。	
江山旅行社☺☺☺☺ 我们一家参加了海南岛五日游。我对这次旅行非常满意。只有一点我觉得江山旅行社还可以做得更好。我们在海南岛的五天，有些天安排的活动很多，一天要去参观五六个地方。有些天安排的活动很少，有一天只花了一小时去看一个景点，别的时间都是自由活动。希望江山旅行社能够把旅游日程安排得更好。	
江山旅行社☺☺☺☺☺ 我和女朋友参加了华北一周游。我们去了四个城市，日程安排得满满的。每天早上八点出发，晚上九点以后才回旅店。我们旅游团的有些游客抱怨说，这样旅游太辛苦，他们觉得很累。我不同意。出来玩就应该好好玩。能这样从早玩到晚，让我非常高兴。要是我们慢慢地玩，就不可能在七天里去四个城市了。	

VIII. 口头报告：坐公交 Oral Report: Using Public Transportation

You need to do online research to complete this activity.

1. Think of a place that you would like to visit in the state/province/city where you live.
2. Do an online search (using online maps or a local transit map, for example) to find out how to get there from where you live by using public transportation.
3. Write down the information that you find.
4. Prepare to make an oral report in Chinese for the next day's class.

IX. 旅游广告 Travel Advertisement

Step 1: Create a travel advertisement, following the models on page 8 of your textbook.

Step 2: Post your advertisement in the designated area in your classroom to create a "travel program exhibit." Read all the advertisements carefully and select one tour package that interests you. Write the details about that travel program in the form below.

这个旅游项目叫什么名字？	
从哪个城市出发？	
哪天出发？	
旅游多少天？	
参观哪些景点？	
需要多少钱？	
包括不包括饮食？	
有没有特价？	
预订热线和网站	

Step 3: Form a small group of three or four people. Tell each other which tour package you have selected and why.

三・写作练习

Based on Activity VII, write an email to your neighbor. In the email, you need to:

1. Summarize the reviews and pinpoint the strengths and weaknesses of each travel agency.
2. Recommend one travel agency to your neighbor, stating why you believe this agency is better than the other one.

Send	Reply	Reply All	Forward	Print	Delete

1.2 卡的世界
A World of Cards

一·听力练习

 I. 连连线! Match Them!

Match the descriptions you hear in Audio Clip 1-2-1 with the terms in Column B. Enter the corresponding numbers in Column A.

A 栏: 请把你听到的写下来	B 栏: 短语的意思
	信用卡
	现金卡
	会员卡
	交通卡
	电话卡
	礼品卡
	生日卡
	借书卡
	学生证
	取款卡

II. 对话一理解 Dialogue 1 Comprehension

Listen to the recording of Dialogue 1 from Lesson 1.2 first, and then answer the True/False questions in Audio Clip 1-2-2.

	1	2	3	4
对				
错				

III. 对话二理解 **Dialogue 2 Comprehension**

Listen to the recording of Dialogue 2 from Lesson 1.2 first, and then answer the True/False questions in Audio Clip 1-2-3.

	1	2	3
对			
错			

 IV. 回答问题 **Answer the Questions**

Answer the questions in this section based on your understanding of the Lesson 1.2 dialogues.

Directions: Listen carefully to the questions in Audio Clip 1-2-4 and record your answers on an audio recorder. You have 20 seconds to record your answers. If you do not have a recording device, arrange with your teacher to leave him/her a voicemail or write down your answers below in pinyin or characters.

1. _____

   _____

2. _____

   _____

3. _____

   _____

4. _____

   _____

5. _____

   _____

6. _____

   _____

V. 怎么回答? Rejoinders

In Audio Clip 1-2-5 you will hear five partial conversations, followed by four possible choices designated (A), (B), (C), and (D). Circle the choice that continues or completes the conversation in a logical and culturally appropriate manner.

Note: Both the questions and the choices will be read only once.

1	2	3	4	5
(A)	(A)	(A)	(A)	(A)
(B)	(B)	(B)	(B)	(B)
(C)	(C)	(C)	(C)	(C)
(D)	(D)	(D)	(D)	(D)

 VI. 这个词是什么意思? **What does this word mean?**

In Audio Clip 1-2-6 you will hear a selection of Chinese terms that have been introduced either in the Lesson 1.2 texts or in the "学无止境" section. After each term, you will be given 20 seconds to record a definition and explanation. Record your answers on an audio recorder. If you do not have a recording device, arrange with your teacher to leave him/her a voicemail or write down your answers below in pinyin or characters.

Model:

You will hear:	You will say:
学生证	这是学校发给学生的证件。用这个证件学生可以买便宜的电影票和火车票。

Terms	Notes
1.	
2.	
3.	
4.	
5.	
6.	
7.	
8.	

 VII. 中国文化短文 **A Short Text on Chinese Culture**

In Audio Clip 1-2-7 a student is giving a presentation based on a famous Chinese creation myth. After listening to the presentation, decide based on its content whether each statement is true or false. The presentation will be played twice. You can take notes while listening.

Below is a word bank that may help you understand the presentation better.

女娲	Nǚ Wā	proper name	绳子	shéngzi	rope, string
女神	nǚshén	goddess	沾	zhān	be stained with
寂寞	jìmò	lonely	洒	sǎ	sprinkle
泥人	nírén	clay figurine			

Notes:

对不对？

	对	错
1. According to this legend, Nü Wa was the first human on earth.		
2. Many Chinese people believe that Pan Gu and Nü Wa created human beings together.		
3. According to this legend, humans were created from loess and water.		
4. In the Chinese creation myth, human beings were created in the image of Nü Wa.		

二·综合语言练习

I. 用汉语怎么说? **How do you say it in Chinese?**

If a word or a phrase is provided, try to use it in your sentence.

1. Look, I have a gift card from the department store. Let's go shopping there.

   _____

   _____

2. My wallet is too small and can't hold so many cards.

   _____

   _____

3. I have too many cards. Here is an ATM card, a credit card, a supermarket membership card, a phone card, and a library card. （这个… 那个… 的）

   _____

   _____

4. It is indeed more convenient to carry a bank card than to carry cash. （的确）

   _____

   _____

5. After you swipe your cafeteria card, you will know the balance on the card.

   _____

   _____

6. To use a debit card, first you need to add money to the card account.

   _____

   _____

7. If by any chance you forget to take the cards, you won't be able to take care of business. （万一）

   _____

   _____

8. Every day there is too much homework. It usually takes me four hours to finish it.
（这个… 那个… 的）

_____

_____

II. 结伴活动：他们有几张卡？ Pair Activity: How many cards do they have?

Based on Dialogue 1 in Lesson 1.2, decide whether Kelly and David have the following cards. You should put a checkmark in the corresponding column. After you have finished, compare your answers with a partner.

卡／证	凯丽	大卫	卡／证	凯丽	大卫
礼品卡			借书证		
电话卡			学生证		
航空公司会员卡			上网卡		
信用卡			现金卡		
银行卡			超市会员卡		
健身房会员卡			手机卡		
饭卡			书店会员卡		
百货公司特价卡			交通卡		

III. 结伴活动：有什么不同？ Pair Activity: What's the difference?

Based on Dialogue 2 in Lesson 1.2, take turns describing the difference between the two items in the left column. If you can't describe the difference, your partner has a chance to try. You will score 1 point for a correct answer and 0 points for no answer or an incorrect answer. At the end of the activity, tally the scores. The one who has the higher total score wins the game.

有什么不同？	你	你同学
会员卡，礼品卡		
现金卡，信用卡		
现金卡，礼品卡		
交通卡，信用卡		
电话卡，交通卡		
学生食堂饭卡，现金卡		
总计 (Total)		

IV. 对不对 True or False?

Based on your understanding of the Lesson 1.2 dialogues, decide whether the following statements are correct.

	对	错
1. 凯丽要去东方百货公司是因为她有一张东方百货公司的礼品卡。		
2. 大卫需要一个大钱包，因为他出门的时候总是带很多钱。		
3. 大卫觉得现在的钱包太小，因为他的钱包放不下很多卡。		
4. 凯丽也有许多卡，所以也需要一个大钱包。		
5. 大卫有三张上海银行的卡。		
6. 不管你有哪种银行卡，都可以去商店买东西。		
7. 银行发的卡都是为了让大家买东西比较方便。		

8. 一个人银行账户上有多少钱决定他可以用现金卡花多少钱。		
9. 大卫觉得用卡办事非常方便，因为卡又小又轻。		
10. 凯丽觉得用卡办事不一定方便，因为带错了卡就办不了事了。		

V. 全班活动：你会怎么做？ **Mixer Activity: What would you do?**

Step 1: Work individually. What would you do if you encountered the following situations? Complete the sentences in Chinese.

万一发生这些情况：	我大概会这么做：
万一我的钱包不见了，	
	跟我的想法一样的同学是：_____ 和 _____
万一这个商店只收现金，	
	跟我的想法一样的同学是：_____ 和 _____
万一我忘了带借书证，	
	跟我的想法一样的同学是：_____ 和 _____
万一我没有超市的会员卡，	
	跟我的想法一样的同学是：_____ 和 _____

Step 2: Circulate around the classroom to interview other students. You need to find at least two people who would take the same action as you in any two situations. Enter their names in the space provided in the worksheet above.

Model: 你： 万一你的钱包不见了，你怎么办？

你同学： 万一我的钱包不见了，我会报告警察。

VI. 小组活动：给你看我的卡 Group Activity: Show and Tell

Step 1: Form a group of three or four. Take turns showing the cards you have with you and describe the use of these cards.

Step 2: Each group reports to the class who in their group has the most and the fewest cards. The one with the most cards should name one advantage of having so many cards. The one with the fewest cards should name one advantage of having very few cards.

VII. 你的意见是什么？ What's your opinion?

There are many opinions about the use of credit cards. Read the following statements and answer the comprehension questions.

第一个人的意见：
我觉得用信用卡买东西是非常聪明的，因为我需要什么马上就可以买，不用等到有钱了再买。比方说，我上了大学以后，需要买一个电脑，我就用信用卡先把电脑买回来，然后再一个月一个月慢慢地还钱。要不是信用卡，我就得等好几个月才能买电脑；这样就会影响我的学习了。

Summarize the first person's opinion in one or two sentences.

第一个人觉得：

_____

_____

第二个人的意见：

在许多国家，有钱人和没钱的人过着非常不同的生活，有钱人什么都能买，没钱人什么都不能买。这样会影响人跟人的关系，造成 (cause) 很多社会问题。比如，没钱的人会觉得生活太不公平了，也会讨厌有钱人。有了信用卡，这个问题就解决了。没很多钱的人也可以买东西。再说，没钱的人不一定是永远 (yǒngyuǎn, forever) 没有钱，特别是年轻人，他们可能因为现在还没开始工作，所以现在没有钱。但是将来他们工作了，就会有钱的。信用卡可以让年轻人今天就用明天的钱，这不是解决社会问题的好方法吗？

Summarize the second person's opinion in one or two sentences.

第二个人觉得：

_____

_____

第三个人的意见：

中国有一句老话，"有多少钱，办多少事。"意思是，如果一个人一个月有1000元钱，就应该生活得象有1000元的人，不应该生活得象有2000元的人。1000元可以住一个小房间，坐公交车上班，自己在家做饭吃。2000元就可以住大一点儿的房子，有时候还可以去饭店吃饭。我觉得这句老话很有道理。每个人都应该对自己做的事负责。现在有些人喜欢用信用卡买东西，也就是说，今天在花明天的钱。这不是让人学坏，变得不负责任吗？所以，我自己不用信用卡，我家里的人也都不用信用卡。

Summarize the third person's opinion in one or two sentences.

第三个人觉得：

_____

_____

第四个人的意见：

我喜欢有信用卡是因为带卡比带现金方便，特别是出门旅行的时候，就不用带许多现金了，只要带一张小小的卡。说到怎么用信用卡，那要看各人了。你可以用，也可以不用，可以多用，也可以少用。大家都应该根据自己的情况，决定什么时候用，用多少。我是一个不喜欢乱花钱的人，所以信用卡对我来说，没有什么坏处。但是如果一个喜欢乱花钱的人有了信用卡，那就比较危险了。

Summarize the fourth person's opinion in one or two sentences.

第四个人觉得：

_____

_____

第五个人的意见：

我要告诉大家我的经验。高中一毕业我就申请了一张信用卡。有了卡买东西太方便了。每次我想买什么，就刷一下卡。可是有一天，我刷卡的时候，营业员告诉我，卡里没钱了，我不能再用信用卡了。这时候我才知道我已经花了太多的钱。后来的几个月，我一直在忙着还钱。我的经验告诉我，用信用卡不一定好，因为你常常不知道自己花了多少钱。

Summarize the fifth person's opinion in one or two sentences.

第五个人觉得：

_____

_____

VIII. 结伴活动：我也觉得太多了 Pair Activity: I agree that there is too much

You and your partner are at a shopping center. After a while, both of you are overwhelmed by the similarities of products you have seen. Use 这个…那个…的 to describe what you have seen. After your partner has spoken, express your agreement by using 的确.

Model: （在购物中心）

A: 这个店那个店的，这里的商店太多了。

B: 你说得对。这里的商店的确太多了。

Step 1: Work individually. Write a comment about each place using 这个…那个…的.

A's Worksheet

在面包房	
在电脑店	
在衣服店	

B's Worksheet

在鞋店	
在冰激凌店	
在电子产品店	

Step 2: Take turns sharing your comments with your partner, and see if s/he agrees with you.

三·写作练习

Based on Activity VII and your personal opinions about the pros and cons of using a credit card, write an essay of 150-200 characters. Your essay should include:

1. A list of the pros and cons of using a credit card;
2. A short explanation of why people think using a credit card is good or bad; and
3. Your recommendation to cardholders.

1.3 日新月异
Rapid Changes

一·听力练习

I. 连连线! Match Them!

Match the descriptions you hear in Audio Clip 1-3-1 with the terms in Column B. Enter the corresponding numbers in Column A.

A 栏： 请把你听到的写下来	B 栏： 句子的意思
	现在还在下雨。
	我说汉语说得比以前好了。
	我到今天才能跟你联系。
	现在我只用信用卡买东西。
	我们学校的老师和学生都不能从前门进学校。
	我们的新宿舍非常方便。
	现在我可以上网了。
	现在在我们的社区，去健身房运动的人一天比一天多了。

II. 课文一理解 Text 1 Comprehension

Listen to the recording of Text 1 from Lesson 1.3 first, and then answer the True/False questions in Audio Clip 1-3-2.

	1	2	3	4
对				
错				

III. 课文二理解 Text 2 Comprehension

Listen to the recording of Text 2 from Lesson 1.3 first, and then answer the True/False questions in Audio Clip 1-3-3.

	1	2	3	4
对				
错				

 IV. 回答问题 Answer the Questions

Answer the questions based on your understanding of the Lesson 1.3 texts.

Directions: Listen carefully to the questions in Audio Clip 1-3-4 and record your answers on an audio recorder. You have 20 seconds to record your answers. If you do not have a recording device, arrange with your teacher to leave him/her a voicemail or write down your answers below in pinyin or characters.

1. _____

_____

2. _____

_____

3. _____

_____

4. _____

_____

5. _____

_____

6. _____

_____

V. 听对话 Listen to the Dialogues

Audio Clip 1-3-5 includes three short conversations. Each conversation is followed by several questions regarding its content. After listening to each dialogue, answer the questions in English. Each dialogue will be played twice.

Dialogue 1

1. Why did the male speaker make the phone call?

_____

2. What suggestions did the female speaker give him?

_____

3. What were the conditions in order for the male speaker to get free wireless equipment?

_____

Dialogue 2

1. What did the woman want to know about the community?

_____

2. Does the community kindergarten admit children from other communities? Why?

_____

3. How is the service charge decided?

_____

Dialogue 3

1. What is the topic of this conversation?

_____

2. What advantages and disadvantages did the male speaker list for houses in different locations?

_____

3. What decision will the male speaker make?

_____

VI. 用汉语怎么解释？ **How do you explain it in Chinese?**

In Audio Clip 1-3-6 you will hear a selection of Chinese terms and phrases about living quarters. After each term or phrase, you will be given 10 seconds to record a definition or explanation. Record your answers on an audio recorder. If you do not have a recording device, you can write down your answers below in pinyin or Chinese characters.

Model:

You will hear:	You will say:
卧室	这是睡觉用的房间。

Notes	Your definition:

VII. 中国文化短文 A Short Text on Chinese Culture

In Audio Clip 1-3-7 a student is giving a presentation based on a famous Chinese myth. After listening to the presentation, decide based on its content whether each statement is true or false. The presentation will be played twice. You can take notes while listening.

Below is a word bank that may help you understand the presentation better.

夸父	Kuā Fù	proper name	渭河	Wèihé	the Wei River
逐日	zhúrì	chase the sun	泽	zé	pond
巨人	jùrén	giant	拐杖	guǎizhàng	walking stick
蛇	shé	snake	桃树	táoshù	peach tree
渴	kě	thirsty			

Notes:

对不对?

	对	错
1. According to this legend, Kua Fu was a giant who ran a race with the Moon.		
2. Kua Fu carries four red snakes.		
3. During the race, Kua Fu drank the water from two rivers to quench his thirst.		
4. Before Kua Fu died, his walking stick turned into orange trees.		

二 · 综合语言练习

I. 用汉语怎么说? How do you say it in Chinese?

If a word or a phrase is provided, try to use it in your sentence.

1. Since they moved to the new residential area, they often go to the community gym.
   （自从…以后）

   _____

2. Workers are repairing the roads. They are going to change the two lanes into three lanes.

   _____

3. High school seniors feel a lot of stress related to their studies and the college entrance exam.

   _____

4. Since this is a new city, it has many construction sites.

   _____

5. How do you get online? Do you use broadband or wireless?

   _____

6. Installing broadband is not easy, because we live in an ancient city.

   _____

7. Last week I finally visited the museum of Chinese ethnic minorities.（终于）

_____

8. He wanted to get a drink from the automatic vending machine, but the machine wouldn't take debit cards.

_____

9. Yesterday she left her cell phone at home and didn't see her friend's text message.

_____

10. Since the community center opened, many residents have attended community activities there.（自从…以后）

_____

II. 凯丽告诉明英什么？ **What did Kelly tell Mingying?**

Based on Text 1 in Lesson 1.3, decide whether Kelly has written to Mingying about the following items.

	写了	没写
1. 虽然明英离开上海才两三个星期，但是大家都想念她。		
2. 为了考上大学，高三学生的学习压力很大。		
3. 这个学期，凯丽搬到新宿舍楼去住了。		
4. 在新宿舍楼，可以无线上网或者用宽带上网。		
5. 新宿舍楼有自动售货机，可以买到饮料和点心。		
6. 现在，除了超市以外，学生还可以去学校旁边的小店买吃的东西。		
7. 现在，学校外边在修马路。		
8. 学校对面要造一个非常大的居民社区。		
9. 因为工人24小时都在工作，所以在凯丽高中毕业以前，社区就能建完。		
10. 虽然上海不是一个新城市，可是每天都有变化。		

III. 明英喜欢大理吗？ **Does Mingying like Dali?**

Read the following list. Based on Text 2 in Lesson 1.3, select which things Mingying likes about Dali.

	大理的这些情况，明英都喜欢吗？
	1. 大理的旁边有一个大湖，可以去游泳。
	2. 大理古城的房子比较旧。
	3. 在旧房子里，没有电话。
	4. 在旧房子里，不能装宽带。
	5. 在旧房子里，可以无线上网。
	6. 大理的古城有六七百年的历史。
	7. 除了古城以外，大理还有新城。
	8. 大理附近有山有水，风景很好。
	9. 大理的气候不错。
	10. 可以坐飞机、火车、汽车去大理。

IV. 小组活动：难做吗？ **Group Activity: Was it hard to do?**

Step 1: Think of three things that you found difficult to do, but that you finally managed to get done. In case you can't think of three, the following list is to give you some ideas.

打篮球	做数学作业	学汉语	滑冰	做饭	放风筝
玩滑板	找工作	做历史作业	踢足球	骑马	做口头报告
弹钢琴	唱歌	听校长报告	养宠物	训练狗	打棒球
学习经济学	看中文书	修车	申请大学	上物理课	滑雪

Step 2: In the space below, describe what was not easy for you to do and how you finally got it done. Be sure to use 终于.

Model: 做中国点心：

我一边看书一边学着做中国点心，终于做出来了。

| |
| |
| |

Step 3: Form a group of four. Share your experience with the group. After each member has spoken, the group selects one of the most interesting or challenging experiences. The person whose experience is selected will share his or her experience in class.

V. 结伴活动：白先生的经验 Pair Activity: Mr. Bell's Experience

Suppose a new Assistant Principal, Mr. Bell（白先生）, has arrived at your school. The Principal has tasked you and your partner with writing a blurb about Mr. Bell and posting it on the school's website. After you have interviewed Mr. Bell, you are now putting your notes together for the blurb.

Step 1: Do you know how to say the following things in Chinese? Write your answers in the spaces below, using 自从…以后.

A's Worksheet

Mr. Bell has been working in high schools since he graduated from college.	
Since he learned how to play the piano at age 6, Mr. Bell has played it almost every day.	
Mr. Bell has been very interested in aliens（外星人）since seeing the movie "Star Wars"（星球大战）.	

B's Worksheet

Mr. Bell has always been interested in basketball since he joined his elementary school's basketball team.	
Since he married a Japanese woman, Mr. Bell has started learning Japanese.	
Mr. Bell has been volunteering in the community library since he moved to the community three years ago.	

Step 2: Take turns telling each other what you know about Mr. Bell. When your partner speaks, listen carefully and write down the main information. After you have finished, compare notes to see if you have written everything down correctly.

Step 3: Work together to write a blurb about Mr. Bell for the school's website.

欢迎白先生！

VI. 小组活动：最佳故事 Group Activity: The Best Story Contest

Step 1: Form a group of three or four. Each group is going to work on a story. The first line of the story is already written. Your group can choose one from the following list to work on. The only requirement is you must use the word 幸亏 to complete the story.

林林打算去学校旁边的小吃店买点儿吃的,可是那个小吃店关门了。	我的小狗看到狗饼干,高兴极了。可是狗饼干在冰箱上,它吃不到。
小平在饭店吃完饭才发现他忘了带钱包了。	大明想给女朋友发短信,可是他的手机没电了。
史明去社区图书馆借书,可是忘了带借书证。	思风想在家装宽带上网,可是他父母觉得没有必要。
那天,老张本来要坐船去看太湖,可是早上起来一看,外边大风大雨,老张不想去了。	校长听说大家对数学课有意见,让我们马上去他的办公室跟他谈话。

Step 2: Share your story in class. The class will vote for the best story.

VII. 小组活动：社区介绍 Group Activity: What does this community have?

Step 1: Form a group of three or four. Find a community that everyone knows something about (e.g. the community you live in, the community where your school is located, a community in your town/city…). Talk about the facilities and characteristics of this community and take notes in the space below.

社区的设施 (shèshī, facilities)	社区的特点

Step 2: Elect one representative to report your findings to the rest of the class. Listen to other groups' reports carefully. Take notes on the differences among the communities.

社区：	社区：	社区：

Step 3: After all the groups have reported, compare notes in class. The student who has listed all the differences wins the title of "Best Observer."

VIII. 连连看！ Match them!

Match the contents of Columns A and C to build a complete sentence.

A	B	C
1. 高三学生总是在担心高考，	也就是说，	a. 做什么事都可以用卡。
2. 这个城市每天都在变化，	也就是说，	b. 他想不做也不行了。
3. 他是骑虎难下，	也就是说，	c. 他们的学习压力非常大。
4. 现在真是卡的世界，	也就是说，	d. 那里的变化日新月异。

答案：

_____

IX. 小对话 Mini-Dialogue

A: You start first. • Greet B. Tell B you haven't seen him/her for a while. • Ask where B lives now. • Ask if B likes the community. • Tell B the community sounds quite modern.	**B: Your partner starts first.** • Greet A. Tell A your family has moved. • Tell A you live in the "New World Community." • Tell A the community has an activity center, a library, a gym, a shopping center… • Tell A although the community is quite modern, you don't like it that much. It is too far from the city center.
A: Your partner starts first. • Tell B that workers are working 24 hours a day. Ask if B has noticed that the workers are constructing a large building. • Tell B you have heard the large building will be an elementary school. • Tell B since your school is here, no new middle school will be built. • Agree with B. Tell B that your school will be repaired during the summer.	**B: You start first.** • Ask if A has noticed that many houses are already built on the construction site next to your school. • Ask A what the large building is for. • Ask A if the community will have a middle school too. • Express your disappointment. Tell A your school building is quite old, you wish you could move to a better building.

三・写作练习

Write an essay in Chinese (150-200 characters) about your community. You might consider including some or all of the following information in your essay:

1. The location of your community,
2. The history of your community,
3. Facilities in your community,
4. People in your community,
5. Characteristics of your community,
6. Well-known sites and businesses in your community, and
7. Any unique things about your community.

1.4 网校
Online School

一·听力练习

 I. 连连线! **Match Them!**

Match the words and phrases you hear in Audio Clip 1-4-1 with the definitions in Column B. Enter the corresponding numbers and phrases in Column A.

A 栏： 请把你听到的写下来	B 栏： 短语的意思
	这样的学校没有真正的校园，只有一个网址。学生们到这个网页上做练习，也可以在网上跟老师见面。
	这是一种帮助学生准备考试的补习班。
	这是在网校里的课堂。学生可以在网上跟网校的老师对话，问问题，等等。
	这种教育一般是在电视上或者在网上进行的。
	这种书告诉学生怎么准备考试，怎么回答考试问题。
	这种书帮助学生分析考试的题目和类型 (type)。
	这个词的意思是准备考试，但是主要是准备申请大学的考试。

II. 对话理解 Dialogue Comprehension

Listen to the recording of the Lesson 1.4 Dialogue first, and then answer the True/False questions in Audio Clip 1-4-2.

	1	2	3	4
对				
错				

 III. 课文理解 Text Comprehension

Listen to the recording of the Lesson 1.4 Text first, and then answer the True/False questions in Audio Clip 1-4-3.

	1	2	3	4
对				
错				

 IV. 回答问题 Answer the Questions

Listen carefully to the questions in Audio Clip 1-4-4 and answer them according to your own situation. Record your answers on an audio recorder. You have 20 seconds to record your answers. If you do not have a recording device, arrange with your teacher to leave him/her a voicemail or write down your answers below in pinyin or characters.

1. _____

_____

2. _____

_____

3. _____

_____

4. _____

_____

5. _____

_____

6. _____

_____

7. _____

_____

V. 听短文 Listen to the Short Passages

Audio Clip 1-4-5 includes three short passages. Each passage is followed by two or three questions based on its content. After listening to each selection, answer the questions in Chinese. Each passage will be read twice.

Passage 1

1. 这个广告是关于什么的?

_____

_____

2. 广告里的服务对什么样的人最适合?

_____

_____

3. 为什么大家应该考虑用广告里的服务?

_____

_____

4. 要是想上网校, 应该怎么跟这个网校联系?

_____

_____

Passage 2

1. 如果你需要给这个报告一个题目, 它应该是什么?

_____

_____

2. 中国的远程教育的历史是怎样的？

_____

_____

3. 网络教学对中国的教育有什么影响？

_____

_____

Passage 3

1. 这里介绍的网校叫什么名字？

_____

_____

2. 为什么从九月以来，报名上网校的人数增加了？

_____

_____

3. 在这个网校，除了同步课堂以外，学生们还可以做什么？

_____

_____

VI. 中国文化短文 A Short Text on Chinese Culture

In Audio Clip 1-4-6 a student is giving a presentation based on a famous Chinese myth. After listening to the presentation, decide based on its content whether each statement is true or false. The presentation will be played twice. You can take notes while listening.

Below is a word bank that may help you understand the presentation better.

炎帝	Yándì	a legendary emperor of China	树枝	shùzhī	twig
淹死	yānsǐ	drown	投	tóu	throw
石子	shízǐ	pebble			

Notes:

对不对？

	对	错
1. According to this fable, Jing Wei was Emperor Yan's favorite bird.		
2. Jing Wei's aspiration was to fill the entire Eastern Sea.		
3. Jing Wei drowned in the Eastern Sea.		
4. This fable tells people that if they work cleverly they will succeed.		

二·综合语言练习

I. 汉语怎么说？ How do you say it in Chinese?

If a word or a phrase is provided, try to use it in your sentence.

1. Whether they are my parents or teachers, everyone says I should strive to go to a good university. （不管）

_____

2. No matter whether it is during the week or on the weekend, many high school students attend the college entrance exam preparation class. （不管）

_____

3. Since everyone is working hard to get ready for the college entrance exam, I have decided to study hard too.

_____

4. I have gotten help from teachers at an online school.

_____

5. Do you know distance learning is not only more convenient but also less expensive?
   （不但…而且…）

_____

6. The online school has synchronized classrooms. If you have questions, you can get answers immediately.

_____

7. We need to read more books and newspapers to understand the world better.

_____

8. Writing a diary in Chinese is a good way to remember new words and practice grammar.

_____

9. When working on math problems, we should learn how to draw inferences.
   （举一反三）

_____

10. Based on the basic principles of math, we can solve (work on) all kinds of difficult problems.
    （根据）

_____

II. 网校 The Online School

After Maria learned about the online school, she sent the following email to several of her friends.

Send	Reply	Reply All	Forward	Print	Delete

大家好!

　　今天汤姆告诉我,为了准备高考,他在上一个网校。那个网校有各种各样的课程和教学辅导材料。除了高中的课程以外,网校还有小学、初中、大学的课程,所以不管你是小学生、中学生还是大学生,都可以去那个网校上课。

　　最酷的是,网校有同步课堂。也就是说,如果你上网修课,不但可以听到老师讲课,还可以上网问问题,马上就可以听到老师的回答。当然,如果你不打算上课,可以把你的问题用电邮发给网校的老师,老师也会马上回答。网校24小时都有老师为学生服务。

　　汤姆还说,如果你们想多练习练习,网上有许多练习题可以做。每次做完了题,网校的老师会发电邮给你,告诉你做得对不对。

　　我打算马上就去那个网校看一下。你们呢?如果你们发现了什么特别的地方,别忘了告诉我。谢谢!

玛丽娅

Based on the Lesson 1.4 Dialogue, decide whether there are any discrepancies between Tom's description and Maria's email. Write these discrepancies in the spaces below. After you have finished, compare notes with a classmate.

汤姆说	玛丽娅说

III. 结对活动：学习方法 Pair Activity: Effective Learning Methods

Step 1: Based on the Lesson 1.4 Text, decide which learning methods are helpful, and for which subject areas. After you have finished, compare notes with a partner.

学习方法	有用	学习科目
上课认真听课		
好好想一想老师提的问题		
看到问题要学会举一反三		
多听，多写，多读，多说		
多背书		
经常写日记或者周记		
记录有用的和好的词句		
作业越多越好		
好好做作业		
多做难题		
常常动笔写有意思的事情		
根据基础题的原理，用不同的方法做难题		
多看书报杂志		
写作文写得短一些，快一些		
把每个生词写十遍		
不要怕说错		
多跟同学练习		

Step 2: Now discuss with your partner which learning methods are useful for you personally. Listen to each answer carefully and take notes. If there are other useful learning methods, you can add them to the list.

学习方法	我觉得有用	我朋友觉得有用
上课认真听课		
好好想一想老师提的问题		
看到问题要学会举一反三		
多听，多写，多读，多说		
多背书		
经常写日记或者周记		
记录有用的和好的词句		
作业越多越好		
好好做作业		
多做难题		
常常动笔写有意思的事情		
根据基础题的原理，用不同的方法做难题		
多看书报杂志		
写作文写得短一些，快一些		
把每个生词写十遍		
不要怕说错		
多跟同学练习		

Step 3: Choose one useful learning method from the list and share it in class. Tell your class:

1. Which learning method is useful for you?
2. What is the result of your using that learning method?
3. Under what circumstances is the learning method most effective?

IV. 结对活动：压力太大 Pair Activity: Too Much Pressure

Lately study pressure is mounting for the senior class, as every teacher tries to prepare you for the college entrance exam by giving you more assignments. Realizing some of the students are stressed out, the high school principal is asking for specific examples of this. Both of you have collected some information. Now you are putting all the facts together for the principal.

Step 1: Do you know how to say the following in Chinese (using 不管···（都）···)? You may write your answers on the worksheet.

Model: The economics teacher wants us to read one book a week no matter whether or not we have time.

不管我们有没有时间，经济学老师都要我们一个星期看一本书。

A's Worksheet

数学课	The math teacher gives us 50 problems a day regardless of whether we have homework from other classes.
英语课	No matter what we have done, the English teacher always says we are not working hard enough.
汉语课	The Chinese teacher asks us to memorize a text a day no matter whether the text is long or short (how long the text is).
历史课	No matter whether it is a weekday or the weekend, the history teacher wants us to write a report a day.

B's Worksheet

数学课	The math teacher wants us to solve three difficult problems a day no matter whether we understand or not.
英语课	No matter when we see the English teacher, he always says we should memorize 50 English words a day.
汉语课	The Chinese teacher puts new characters in the test no matter whether we have learned them or not.
历史课	The history test is very long no matter whether or not there is enough class time.

Step 2: Take turns telling each other what you have found. Take notes on what your partner says. After you have finished, compare notes with your partner.

Model: A: 经济学课的情况怎么样？

B: 不管我们有没有时间，经济学老师都要我们一个星期看一本书。

V. 全班活动：你觉得有道理吗？ Mixer Activity: Does it make sense to you?

The principal would like to gather feedback from students about certain academic practices at your school. Your task is to find out whether there is any consensus among your fellow students.

Step 1: Fill out the following questionnaire on your own. Make sure (1) that you understand the statements, and (2) that you are able to say the statements in Chinese. If you need help, consult your teacher or a classmate.

问卷		
为了改进教学，校长希望了解你对以下的情况有什么意见。谢谢你的帮助！		
	有道理	没有道理
1. 学生每天最少应该做五个小时的作业。		
2. 学生每天最多应该做三个小时的作业。		
3. 每一门课一天可以给一个小时的作业。		
4. 上课的时候学生应该认真听课，不能随便做自己想做的事。		
5. 学习数学最好的方法是多做难题。		
6. 学习数学最好的方法是多做基础题。		
7. 学生应该学会背书，因为背书是学习的好方法。		
8. 不会背书的学生学不好历史课。		
9. 学习地理、化学、物理、外语，都需要背书。		
10. 外语课应该让学生多学语法，多做语法练习。		
11. 外语课应该多让学生看外语电影。		

12. 汉语课应该学习写汉字。		
13. 汉语课的书面作业可以用电脑写。		
14. 学生应该每天都写日记。如果用外语写，更有用。		
15. 老师应该教学生在学习中怎么举一反三。		
16. 每门课每个学期都应该有考试。		
17. 考试不及格的学生应该再上一遍那门课。		
18. 上课讨论的时候，每个学生都应该说话。		
19. 每门课每个学期最少应该让学生写两个报告。		
20. 学生上网做研究是一种很有用的学习方法。		

Step 2: Choose nine statements from the questionnaire above that make sense to you. Write them in the bingo grid below, one statement per cell.

Step 3: Circulate around the classroom to collect your classmates' views. You may ask each classmate one question at a time. If s/he agrees with you, you can cross the cell out. The first one who crosses out three cells in a row (horizontal, vertical, or diagonal) wins the game.

Model: A: 你觉得汉语课应该学写汉字有道理吗？

B: 我觉得有道理。

VI. 口头报告：网上课程 Oral Report: An Online Course

Step 1: Search for an online course and prepare an oral report in Chinese. The following table is to help you organize your presentation, or you can develop your own presentation outline.

网上课程的名字	
网上课程的内容	
网址	
老师（谁上课）	
学生（适合哪些学生）	
上课的方法	
课程的时间	
课本	
考试方法	
帮助（老师帮助和技术帮助）	
学费	
联系方法	
其他	

Step 2: Make an oral presentation about the online course in class.

VII. 结对活动：小对话 Pair Activity: Mini-Dialogue

A	B
You start. • Tell B you are taking an online English reading course. • Tell B you see little difference. You do the reading before going online. • Tell B you have to take an online quiz. The website lets you know immediately whether you have answered correctly. • Tell B you would have to read the article and take the quiz again. When you pass the quiz, you will get a new reading assignment.	**Your partner starts.** • Ask A what differences there are between an online and a regular courses. • Ask how the teacher knows that A has done the reading assignment. • Ask what happens if A makes a lot of mistakes on the quiz. • Tell A an online reading course makes a lot of sense.
Your partner starts. • Congratulate B. Tell B you find memorizing Chinese characters difficult. • Ask what learning methods B is using to memorize Chinese characters. • Ask if B finds practicing boring? • Ask if B only writes about her/his life? • Tell B that sounds like a good practice. Maybe you will start with writing a weekly journal in Chinese.	**You start.** • Tell A you are happy you did well on the Chinese test. • Tell A you had the same difficulty before, but now you are better at memorizing characters. • Tell A you often write the characters. • Tell A you don't just write the characters, you use Chinese to write a diary. • Tell A you not only write about your life, but also about the good books you have read.

VIII. 学汉语的好方法 Tips for Learning Chinese

Since you have learned Chinese for several years, your Chinese teacher would like you to offer some learning tips to the freshman Chinese class. The teacher has given you a list of questions from the freshmen class and asked you to select two questions that you can answer.

• 我们一个星期要记住二十多个生词。有什么记住生词的好方法吗？
• 我们的汉语考试有一些语法题，你平时怎么练习语法？
• 每次看课文，都有几个我不认识的字。你每次看到不认识的字都查字典吗？

- 看课文的时候，需要不需要把每个句子都翻译成英文？

- 怎么才可以记住汉字呢？我常常写了左边，忘了右边。写了上边，忘了下边。

- 听写的时候，录音很快，我没有时间把每个字写下来。有什么好方法吗？

- 老师让我们每天用中文写日记。写日记对学汉语有哪些好处？

- 你们常常去中文网站吗？哪些中文网站比较有用，也比较有意思？

- 你用汉英词典吗？哪本汉英词典最好用？如果你知道网上的汉英词典，也请告诉我。

三·写作练习

Based on Activity VIII, write detailed answers to the two questions you have selected. The teacher would like to post your answers online. Apart from giving a straightforward answer, you are asked to add an example from your own learning experience. Limit each answer to 140 characters.

1.5 新图书馆
A New Library

 I. 连连线! Match Them!

Match the words and phrases you hear in Audio Clip 1-5-1 with the definitions in Column B. Enter the corresponding numbers and phrases in Column A.

A 栏: 请把你听到的写下来	B 栏: 短语的意思
	这样的书和报纸是在网上的。
	这是在图书馆里看书报和杂志的房间。
	这种书包括字典，一般不可以从图书馆里借走，只可以在图书馆里用。
	这种卡常常是在图书馆或者学校里用的。在很多图书馆里，要是你想打印，你一定要有这种卡。
	在很多中国的图书馆里，要是你看自然科学的书和杂志，你可能会去这个阅览室。
	这是在图书馆里看录像、听录音的地方。

II. 对话一理解 Dialogue 1 Comprehension

Listen to the recording of Dialogue 1 from Lesson 1.5 first, and then answer the True/False questions in Audio Clip 1-5-2.

	1	2	3	4
对				
错				

 III. 对话二理解 Dialogue 2 Comprehension

Listen to the recording of Dialogue 2 from Lesson 1.5 first, and then answer the True/False questions in Audio Clip 1-5-3.

	1	2	3	4
对				
错				

 IV. 即时对话 Simulated Conversation

You are working as a volunteer at your local library. Now you are talking to a customer, who is calling to inquire about the library's services and hours. Listen carefully to the customer's questions in Audio Clip 1-5-4, and then answer them according to the library information sheet below. After each question, you will have 20 seconds to record your answers. If you do not have a recording device, you can arrange with your teacher to leave him/her a voicemail or write down your answers below in pinyin or characters.

各厅室位置及开放时间		
◇ 一层 ◇		
◆ 书报阅览室	◆ 借书部	◆ 客户服务部
周一　　　　14:00–20:30 周二至周日　09:00–20:30	周一　　　　14:00–20:30 周二至周日　09:00–20:30	周一　　　　14:00–20:30 周二至周日　09:00–20:30
◇ 二层 ◇		
◆ 多媒体阅览室及 　电脑中心	◆ 参考书阅览室	◆ 自习室
周一　　　　14:00–20:30 周二至周日　09:00–20:30	周一　　　　14:00–20:30 周二至周日　09:00–20:30	周一至周四 14:00–20:30 周五至周日 09:00–17:30
◆ 第一阅览室	◆ 音乐室	◆ 复印中心
周一　　　　14:00–20:30 周二至周日　09:00–20:30	周二至周四 09:00–20:30 周五、周六 09:00–17:30	周一至周日 14:00–20:30 （复印需要用电脑服 务卡）
◇ 三层 ◇		
◆ 多媒体阅览室及 　电脑中心	◆ 第二阅览室	◆ 自习室
周一　　　　14:00–20:30 周二至周日　09:00–20:30	周一　　　　14:00–20:30 周二至周日　09:00–20:30	周一至周四 14:00–20:30 周五至周日 09:00–17:30

1. _____

2. _____

3. _____

4. _____

5. _____

6. _____

V. 听短文 **Listen to the Short Passages**

Audio Clip 1-5-5 includes three short passages. Each passage is followed by two or three questions based on the content. After listening to each passage, answer the questions in Chinese. Each passage will be read twice.

Passage 1

1. 如果要办理电脑服务卡，应该去几楼?

_____

2. 这个图书馆有几个多媒体阅览室?

_____

3. 如果想借用自习教室，要带什么证件?

_____

Passage 2

1. 这里介绍的是什么样的图书馆?

_____

2. 在这个图书馆看不到什么样的作品?

_____

3. 这个图书馆现在收藏了多少古典音乐的作品?

_____

Passage 3

1. 这里介绍的图书馆是什么时候开馆的?

_____

2. 这个图书馆一共有多少书报杂志?

_____

3. 如果你想借的书图书馆里没有怎么办?

_____

4. 除了借书还书的服务以外，这个图书馆还有什么服务?

_____

 VI. 中国文化短文 **A Short Text on Chinese Culture**

In Audio Clip 1-5-6 a student is giving a presentation based on a famous Chinese creation myth. After listening to the presentation, decide based on its content whether each statement is true or false. The presentation will be played twice. You can take notes while listening.

Below is a word bank that may help you understand the presentation better.

仓颉	Cāng Jié	proper name	树枝	shùzhī	twig
黄帝	Huángdì	a legendary king of China	豹子	bàozǐ	leopard
统一	tǒngyī	unify	启发	qǐfā	inspire
凤凰	fènghuáng	phoenix	第一批	dìyīpī	the first batch
树叶	shùyè	tree leaf	象形字	xiàngxíngzì	pictographs
脚印	jiǎoyìn	footprint			

Notes:

对不对?

	对	错
1. Cang Jie decided to create Chinese characters in order to make it easier for the people who live along the Yellow River to engage in trade.		
2. Cang Jie was inspired to invent the Chinese writing system when he saw the tracks left by a phoenix.		
3. According to Cang Jie, although all things in the world have their own shapes and sizes, the writing system should resemble the sound of an utterance.		
4. The first characters that Cang Jie created are called "pictographs."		

二·综合语言练习

Ⅰ. 用汉语怎么说? How do you say it in Chinese?

If a word or a phrase is provided, try to use it in your sentence.

1. The new library has many automated services.

_____

2. The high-rise has four elevators. Going up and down is fast and convenient. (又…又…)

_____

3. Now you can use the library's online catalogue.

_____

4. If a book is checked out by someone else, you can check when the return date is.

_____

5. You can also make a reservation for the book that you would like to check out.

_____

6. The library has several reading rooms for digital books, magazines, and newspapers.

_____

7. Aside from the reference reading room, the library also has a multi-media reading room. （除外）

_____

8. You need to buy a computer service card if you want printing and copying services.

_____

9. Every student in our school can use the library. （凡是…都…）

_____

10. Every lecture and activity this semester is (listed) in the computer. （凡是…都…）

_____

II. 新图书馆 The New Library

You saw a few messages about the new library. Based on Dialogue 1 in Lesson 1.5, decide whether each message gives the same or different information about the new library.

	一样	不同
国际学校的新图书馆很大，有六楼。		
在新图书馆坐电梯不太方便，因为电梯很慢。		
要借书必须去图书馆用图书馆的电脑查信息。		
新图书馆借书都自动化了。		
新图书馆的书报比以前增加了很多。		
新图书馆有许多地方可以让学生学习。		

III. 图书馆的服务 Library Services

Based on Dialogue 2 in Lesson 1.5, decide whether the new library provides the following services.

新图书馆有这些服务吗？	有	没有
• 图书馆有参考书。		
• 图书馆有汉语和各种外语的参考书。		
• 图书馆有参考阅览室。		
• 每次可以从图书馆借三本参考书。		
• 可以在图书馆的电脑室免费上网。		
• 图书馆有外文阅览室。		
• 在图书馆的多媒体阅览室，可以看中国和外国的报纸。		
• 图书馆有视听阅览室。		
• 可以从图书馆借电影、音乐、电脑软件的光盘。		
• 图书馆每天都有讲座。		
• 可以用电脑查图书馆目录。		
• 谁都可以预订图书馆的学习室和大教室。		
• 图书馆的网络学习室有电脑和打印机。		
• 在图书馆可以免费打印。		
• 在图书馆可以买上网卡、电话卡、电脑服务卡。		

IV. 结对活动：哪个词？ Pair Activity: Name That Word

Take turns describing the following phenomena with a word ending with 化. If you can't think of a word, your partner has the chance to try. At the end of the game, tally the scores. The one with a higher total score wins the game.

Model: 现在一些学校不关心教学，只想多收学费，多赚钱。—商业化

	你	你同学
1. 让一个地方变得更美丽。		
2. 很多国家在学习西方国家，希望变得跟西方国家差不多。		
3. 以前这些事情要人动手去做，现在不需要动手了。		
4. 这个村子变得越来越像城市了。		
5. 这个公司的服务越来越注意每个人不同的需要。		
6. 我们学校以前有许多老教师，现在年轻的老师越来越多了。		
7. 这些工作现在都可以由电脑去做。		
8. 一些大公司在世界各国做生意。		
9. 现在不少杂志关心的不是杂志的内容，是怎么赚更多的钱。		
10. 世界上越来越多的人用手机。		
总分		

V. 小组活动：惯例 Group Activity: Common Practices

Step 1: Work individually. Think of three common practices in your country—things almost everyone does or things that almost always happen. Write these common practices in the space provided below, following the model.

Model: 凡是星期天，银行都不开门。

1.	
2.	
3.	

Step 2: Form a group of three. Take turns describing each of the common practices you have written about. If the group agrees it is a common practice, you can record it in the space below.

1.	
2.	
3.	
4.	
5.	
6.	
7.	
8.	
9.	

Step 3: In class, take turns sharing the common practices the group agreed upon, one practice at a time. The rule is that you can't repeat what has already been said. If you do, you are out of the game.

VI. 结对活动：我们的图书馆 Pair Activity: Our Library

A: On your way to the newly-opened community library, you meet your friend. Since this is your first trip, you'd like to know what the library has to offer. Your friend has been there several times. Ask your friend about the library's business hours, collection of materials, services, and the layout of the building.	B: On your way to the community library, you meet your friend who has never been to the library before. Since you have been there several times, you know the library quite well. Try to answer your friend's questions, including as many details as possible.
A: You have been volunteering at the "Computer Services Desk" of the public library. Now a customer who has just moved to your town would like to know what computer-related services the library provides. Describe the services, including as many details as possible.	B: You have recently moved to a new town. This is your first trip to the town's public library. You would like to know what computer services the library provides, such as the Internet, multi-media resources, on-line catalogues, and other services. Find out as much information as possible.

VII. 结对活动：大楼的布局 Pair Activity: Building Layouts

Suppose your school will host an event for outside visitors next weekend. Classroom Building 1 and the Student Activity Center will be used for the event. You two are on the organization committee and are given a task to draw a map for the visitors. Both you and your partner have walked through the buildings. Now you are comparing notes to make sure that you have all the information about the buildings.

Record any discrepancies between your observations in the spaces provided below.

一号教学大楼		学生活动中心	
A	B	A	B

A's Notes

You like to write down what you see. Here is what you have written about the layout of the two buildings.

一号教学大楼

进门有一个大厅，左边有八个教室（101-108）。右边有四个教师办公室和四个教室（110-117）。在大楼的两边有两个楼梯 (stairs) 可以上下。大厅里有两个电梯，大厅的右边还有一个大会议室（109）。

学生活动中心

进门有一个大厅。大厅里可以开会。左边是学生书店和学生服务中心。右边是咖啡馆、四个活动室和两个办公室。

B's Sketches

You like to draw what you see. Here is what you have drawn to show the layout of the two buildings.

一号教学大楼

楼梯	男厕所	教室 101	教室 103	教室 105	大会议室	电梯	电梯	办公室	办公室	教室	楼梯
	女厕所	教室 102	教室 104	教室 106		大厅		办公室	办公室	教室	

学生活动中心

学生服务中心	男厕所	女厕所	小卖部				
	大厅		咖啡馆				
学生书店			活动室	活动室	活动室	活动室

VIII. 口头报告：我们社区的公共场所 **Oral Report: Public Places in Our Community**

Step 1: Search online for a public place in your community (library, museum, park, recreational center, for example). Take notes on what you have found out about that place and prepare an oral report in Chinese. The following table is to help you organize your presentation, or you can develop your own presentation outline.

公共场所 (place) 的名字	
地址	
开放时间	
提供的服务	
特别的服务	
特点	
适合哪些人去	
其他	

Step 2: Make an oral presentation in class.

三 · 写作练习

Based on Activity VIII, write a short description of the public place in Chinese. Your description will be placed on your city's Tourist Information website. Give a clear description, in some detail, of things you feel visitors would like to know. Your description should contain at least 100 characters.

1.6 第一单元复习
Review of Unit 1

一 · 听力练习

 成语练习

In Audio Clip 1-6-1 you will hear a selection of Chinese idioms and proverbs that have been previously introduced. After each idiom or proverb, you will be given 10 seconds to record a definition or explanation. Record your answers on an audio recorder. If you do not have a recording device, you can write down your answers below in pinyin or Chinese characters.

Word Bank

四通八达	四面八方	比比皆是	不计其数
天翻地覆	一日千里	捷足先登	后来居上

Model:

You will hear:	You will say:
望子成龙	这个成语的意思是父母都希望子女很成功。

Notes	Your definition:

二·口头报告

Choose one of the topics from the list below to give an oral presentation in class.

Topic 1: 我最喜欢的旅游点

Topic 2: 保护环境，请用公共交通

Topic 3: 小小的信用卡改变了我们的生活

Topic 4: 网校为学习提供了方便

Topic 5: 欢迎使用我们学校的图书馆

Topic 6: 互联网对我们生活的影响

After you have chosen a topic, please write an outline for your presentation. You can write the outline on a separate sheet of paper. If your teacher allows, you can also transfer the outline to an index card as a reminder when you give the presentation.

Your presentation must meet the following criteria:

1. It must have a beginning, a middle, and an end.
2. It must include as much detail as possible.
3. It must last no longer than two minutes.

三·综合语言练习

I. 对话理解 Comprehension Questions

Based on the Lesson 1.6 Dialogue, answer the following questions. You may jot down the main points in the space provided.

1. 为什么汤姆用"快"字来总结现代生活？

_____

_____

_____

_____

2. 为什么玛丽娅用"小"字来总结现代生活？

_____

_____

_____

_____

3. 为什么大卫用"冷"字来总结现代生活？

_____

_____

_____

_____

4. 为什么凯丽用"多"字来总结现代生活？

_____

_____

_____

_____

_____

5. 要是让你用一个字来总结现代生活，你会用哪个字？

_____

_____

_____

_____

_____

II. 对不对？ **True or False?**

Based on the Lesson 1.6 Text, figure out whether the following statements are true or false.

	对	错
1. 美国中部的一个高中有一个"中国：网络电话俱乐部"。		
2. 这个俱乐部是在北京一个高中的帮助下成立的。		
3. 这个俱乐部的成立是美国和中国两位高中校长讨论的结果。		
4. 这个俱乐部可以让中美的高中生用网络技术互相学习，互相帮助。		
5. 俱乐部里的每个美国学生都跟中国学生联系过两次了。		
6. 通过俱乐部，美国学生帮助中国学生学习英语。		
7. 通过俱乐部，中国学生帮助美国学生学习汉语。		
8. 中美学生还在一起讨论高中的课程、课外活动等等。		
9. 俱乐部的美国学生都已经访问过中国了。		
10. 中国学生正在打算访问美国。		

III. 结对活动：哪个不对? Pair Activity: Find the Odd One

The four words in each row below are all related in meaning, except one. Find the one that doesn't belong. After you have finished, compare notes with a partner.

通车	村子	马路	车道
阅览室	图书目录	书报杂志	打印
公司	宽带	无线上网	网络
社区	住房	自动售货机	居民
工人	工地	变化	建设
历史	日新月异	古城	古建筑
交通卡	饭卡	电话卡	信用卡
帐户	现金卡	钱包	取款
轻轨	导游	机场专线车	飞机
网络电话	高中生	课程	考试
同步课堂	网校	远程教育	积极
几何	动笔	周记	日记

IV. 全班活动：学习方法 Mixer Survey: Effective Learning Methods

One student has posted "My Ten Most Effective Learning Methods" on a website.

Step 1: Choose three methods that you think are NOT helpful for you.

十种对我最好的学习方法
1.不管是数学、物理、化学还是历史、地理、经济学，最好的学习办法是背书。
2.上课听不懂的时候，马上问老师。
3.学外语最好的方法是多说，多听，多看，多写。
4.做题的时候，如果那个问题不懂，就别马上做。懂了以后再做。
5.凡是那些在高考里可能会有的难题，都应该做三四遍。
6.不管每天做了什么，都写在日记里。这样对练习写作有好处。
7.看书的时候，凡是生词都查词典。
8.上网做研究又快又方便，不用去图书馆做研究了。
9.有问题的时候，不仅可以问老师，也可以问同学。
10.为了准备考试，可以背上课做的笔记。

Step 2: Walk around the classroom and interview your classmates. You may ask each classmate one question at a time. Once you have found two classmates who agree that the three learning methods you selected are NOT helpful, you can stop interviewing. The student who stops interviewing first wins the game.

Model: 你： 我觉得，看书的时候，凡是生词都查词典不是一种好的学习方法。你说呢？

你同学：我同意 or 我不同意。

V. 结对活动：拼句子 Pair Activity: Board Game

Pair up with a partner. Use the words provided on each line to form a sentence. Write down your sentences. The one who reaches FINISH first with all of the sentences correct wins the game.

。	,	服务卡	复印	不管	电脑	需要	都	打印	还是	▼
Regardless of printing or copying, a computer service card is needed.										▼
										▼
。	,	去年	工地	这里	三月	从	就	以来	成了	建筑	▼
Since last March, this place has become a construction site.										▼
										▼
。	,	不管	在	变化	来	上海	你	看到	什么	都	时候	能	▼
No matter when you come, (you) can see Shanghai is changing.										▼
										▼
。	信用卡	买	用	很	的确	东西	方便	▼
It is indeed convenient to use a credit card to buy things.								▼
								▼
。	,	这个	那个	阅览室	阅览室	图书馆	大	的	新	极了	▼
There are so many reading rooms, (and) the new library is very big.										▼
										▼
。	,	可以	自动	万一	买	东西	要	售货机	用	你	▼
In case you want to buy things, (you) can use the automatic vending machine.										▼
										▼
FINISH										

VI. 结对活动 Pair Activity

Situation 1

A:	B:
Your old neighbor who has moved away several years ago is visiting you this weekend. Tell your old neighbor that your community has gone through a lot of changes since s/he moved. Tell him/her about the new roads, shops, houses, residents, services…	Your family moved away several years ago. Now you are visiting your old neighbor. You have found a lot of changes in the community where you used to live. Ask your old neighbor about the changes you see (roads, shops, houses, residents, services…)

Situation 2

A:	B:
You would like to enroll in a College Entrance Exam Preparation course. Ask your friend if s/he knows any good courses. Flexibility and teaching methods are the two most important things for you. Gather as much information from your friend as possible.	You are currently enrolled in an online College Entrance Exam Preparation class. You like the class a lot. Tell your friend why you like it (the curriculum, the teachers, the teaching methods, the time flexibility…)

第二单元 民以食为天

UNIT 2　Bread Is the Staff of Life

2.1　农业和饮食
Agriculture and Food

一·听力练习

I. 连连线! Match Them!

Match the words and phrases you hear in Audio Clip 2-1-1 with the definitions in Column B. Enter the corresponding numbers and phrases in Column A.

A 栏： 请把你听到的写下来	B 栏： 短语的意思
	这个词的意思是一个地区主要的经济是农业。
	这种食品主要是用小麦做的。
	这个词的意思是书、电影、讲座等等的内容很没有意思，不吸引人。
	这是让学生到公司、工厂、或者农村了解情况。
	这个国家很大，它的主要经济是农业。
	这句话的意思是吃饭是生活里最重要的事。
	这样的东西有小麦、大米、玉米、麦片、豆类等等。
	这种经济的主要收入是从农业上得到的。

II. 对话一理解 Dialogue 1 Comprehension

Listen to the recording of Dialogue 1 from Lesson 2.1 first, and then answer the True/False questions in Audio Clip 2-1-2.

	1	2	3	4
对				
错				

 III. 对话二理解 Dialogue 2 Comprehension

Listen to the recording of Dialogue 2 from Lesson 2.1 first, and then answer the True/False questions in Audio Clip 2-1-3.

	1	2	3	4
对				
错				

 IV. 回答问题 Answer the Questions

Listen carefully to the questions in Audio Clip 2-1-4 and answer them according to your own situation. Record your answers on an audio recorder. You have 20 seconds to record your answers. If you do not have a recording device, arrange with your teacher to leave him/her a voicemail or write down your answers below in pinyin or characters.

1. _____

2. _____

3. _____

4. _____

5. _____

6. _____

V. 听对话和短文 Listening Comprehension

Audio Clip 2-1-5 includes three short selections, a dialogue and two passages. Each selection is followed by two or three questions based on its content. After listening to each dialogue or passage, answer the questions in Chinese. Each selection will be read twice.

Dialogue

1. 这个人的饮食中，油、盐、糖占百分之几？

_____

2. 为什么这个人的饮食里没有奶制品？

_____

Passage 1

1. 城市居民的平均收入比农村居民的多多少元？

_____

2. 城市居民平均收入的增加速度比农村居民的快百分之几？

_____

Passage 2

1. 2009年，中国用互联网的人占百分之几？

_____

2. 跟美国比，中国用互联网的人比美国少百分之几？

_____

3. 韩国用互联网的人比美国多百分之几？

_____

VI. 中国文化短文 **A Short Text on Chinese Culture**

In Audio Clip 2-1-6 a student is giving a presentation based on a famous Chinese holiday legend. After listening to the presentation, decide based on its content whether each statement is true or false. The presentation will be played twice. You can take notes while listening.

Below is a word bank that may help you understand the presentation better.

赏月	shǎngyuè	enjoy the Moon	蒙古人	Měnggǔrén	Mongolian
馅儿	xiànr	stuffing	统治	tǒngzhì	rule
莲蓉	liánróng	lotus seed paste	推翻	tuīfān	overthrow
切开	qiēkāi	cut open	起义	qǐyì	uprising
元朝	Yuán Cháo	Yuan Dynasty (AD 1271–1368)	利用	lìyòng	use

Notes:

对不对?

	对	错
1. The Chinese often put an egg yolk inside moon cakes, because they symbolize the moon.		
2. Legend has it that the Chinese used to put party invitations into moon cakes.		
3. Moon cakes were credited with delivering a message about an uprising.		
4. Moon cakes are usually eaten during the Lunar New Year.		

二·综合语言练习

I. 用汉语怎么说？ **How do you say it in Chinese?**

If a word or a phrase is provided, try to use it in your sentence.

1. The economics course is not dry at all, because the teacher often takes us on field trips.（一点儿也不）

    _____

2. In fact, it is hard to imagine what China was like thirty years ago.（实际上）

    _____

3. China's industrialization didn't begin until the end of the 19th century.

    _____

4. China has had an agricultural economy for over 5000 years.（…来）

    _____

5. Because China has many mountainous areas, it doesn't have a lot of farmland.

    _____

6. It is not easy to support 20% of the world's population on 7% of the world's farmland.

    _____

7. Now some farmland has been used to build houses and roads.

    _____

8. Some farmers have become construction workers, some work in factories, and others maintain (work on) green areas.（有的）

    _____

9. Some farmers have signed contracts with restaurants. They provide special vegetables to restaurants.（不同一般）

    _____

10. Some villagers process vegetables first and then sell them to supermarkets.

    _____

II. 凯丽理解得对不对？ **Did Kelly get the facts right?**

After talking to Tom, Kelly told David what she learned from Tom. Based on Dialogue 1 in Lesson 2.1, decide whether the information given by Kelly was correct.

	对	错
1. 经济课非常有意思，除了上课以外，学生还去做校外考察。		
2. 五千多年来，中国的经济主要是农业经济。		
3. 现在中国现代化了，多数地区都是大楼、商场和公司。		
4. 中国工业化有两百年的历史。		
5. 中国的人口和耕地都占世界的百分之二十。		
6. 中国因为人口很多，所以一直努力发展农业来解决人民的吃饭问题。		
7. 中国南方和北方生产的粮食不一样。		
8. 中国的南方人和北方人吃的粮食不一样。		

III. 结对活动：村民的生活 Pair Activity: A Villager's Life

Based on Dialogue 2 in Lesson 2.1, decide whether the following statements describe the villagers' life. Add a √ next to any statement that does.

1. 现在村民住在公寓楼里。	
2. 以前村民种蔬菜，现在都不种了。	
3. 有些村民在工厂工作，有些是建筑工人，有些做绿化工作。	
4. 因为绿化工作是种花，跟种菜差不多，所以村民都很喜欢绿化工作。	
5. 村民都在浦东上班，因为浦东有不少工厂和公司。	
6. 有些村民喜欢自行车运动。	

7. 有些村民早上去菜场卖菜。	
8. 还有些村民在超市和饭店工作。	
9. 有些村民做食品加工的工作。	
10. 村民们都很喜欢买超市里"新浦东"牌的食品。	

IV. 结对活动：实际上⋯ **Pair Activity: In fact...**

Step 1: Based on what you know about your partner, write five sentences to describe him or her (what s/he likes and dislikes, habits, characteristics, etc.)

Model: 最喜欢的运动是骑自行车。
不喜欢上数学课。

	Notes
1.	
2.	
3.	
4.	
5.	

Step 2: Following the model, take turns asking and answering one question at a time. Listen carefully to what your partner says about you. When your partner answers, take notes on whether your partner agrees with your statement, by putting a √ for agreement and an X for disagreement.

Model: 你： 你最喜欢的运动是骑自行车吧？
你同学：对。
 or
不。实际上，我最喜欢的运动是游泳。

V. 小组活动：总的来说 Group Activity: In summary...

Form a group of four. Assign a letter to each person (A, B, C, or D).

Step 1: Look at your column. Make sure you know how to say the statements in Chinese.

	A:	B:	C:	D:
1	For more than 5000 years, the Chinese have been developing agriculture.	China's economy was primarily an agricultural economy.	Most parts of China are still agricultural areas.	总的来说
2	总的来说	China has a lot of mountains and not a lot of plains.	China has a large population, constituting 20% of the world's population.	China has 7% of the world's arable land.
3	In the 1990s, many factories and companies moved to Pudong.	总的来说	Many farmers have become factory workers, construction workers, or groundskeepers.	Not too many farmers are still growing vegetables.
4	Some farmers sell vegetables in the vegetable market.	Some farmers sell their vegetables directly to restaurants and supermarkets.	总的来说	Some farmers process their vegetables before selling then to supermarkets.

Step 2: Take turns being the one who gives the final summary. After the three other group members have made their statements, you will summarize the main ideas. Your summary should start with 总的来说.

VI. 结对活动：很久来都是这么做的 Pair Activity: This has been done for a long, long time

Work with a partner. Try to match the timeframe and the corresponding phenomenon in the table below.

1. 五千多年来	A. 中国的经济成了世界经济的一部分。
2. 一百多年来	B. 电视在大家的娱乐生活中，变得越来越重要。
3. 三千多年来	C. 工业化给中国带来了很大的变化。
4. 三十多年来	D. 中国人一直种茶，喝茶。
5. 七十多年来	E. 黄河旁边一直住着中国人。
6. 四千多年来	F. 中国人用汉字写文章。

答案：

VII. 小组活动：庆祝多元化！ Group Activity: Celebrate Diversity!

Step 1: Form a group of three or four. Select a class, a school, a town, an industry, a country, or a region in the world that is a good example of diversity.

Step 2: Gather some facts/statistics about the place you have selected. Use the space provided below to describe the facts by using 占.

Model:　我们学校的外国学生占百分之十。

我们学校的少数民族学生占百分之二十五。

我们学校会说外语的学生占百分之十五…

Step 3: Each group makes an oral presentation in class.

VIII. 从茶说起 All About Tea

After reading the email Kelly sent to David, answer the comprehension questions.

Send	Reply	Reply All	Forward	Print	Delete

大卫：你好！

记得你问过我，杭州有没有什么特别的博物馆。周末我在杭州的时候，找到了一个非常特别的博物馆：中国茶叶 (yè, leaf) 博物馆。我跟两位英国朋友一起去参观了那个博物馆，学到了不少关于茶叶的知识。

茶叶博物馆在一个很大的茶园中，就像是一个大公园。博物馆不但介绍了中国人种茶和加工茶叶的历史，而且还介绍了跟茶有关的文化活动。

中国人喝茶已经有四千多年的历史了。传说在公元前2737年，有一天神农皇帝 (也就是炎帝) 打算喝点儿开水 (boiled water)。正在这个时候一些树叶从树上掉 (diào, fall) 进了烧水的锅子里，神农喝了以后，觉得非常好喝，就开始在他喝的开水里放一些这样的树叶。这些树叶就是茶叶。慢慢喝茶的人越来越多，茶成了中国人最爱喝的饮料。

从那时候开始，中国人就开始种茶。茶树的生长需要一个比较湿热的地方，冬天不能太冷，夏天也不能太热，而且那个地方最好一年四季都下雨。另外，山地也比较适合茶树的生长。我想这就是为什么杭州附近有不少茶农，因为这里的气候和地理都适合种茶。

我们参观完以后，在博物馆的茶室里喝了杭州生产的绿茶。我们一边谈话，一边看着一片一片绿色的茶叶在开水里慢慢地变大，真是非常有趣。

如果你有兴趣，下次来杭州，也可以去看一看。

凯丽

问题

1. 中国茶叶博物馆在哪个城市？

_____

_____

2. 茶叶博物馆介绍了哪些跟茶有关的情况？

_____

_____

3. 根据传说，中国人是什么时候开始喝茶的？

_____

_____

4. 茶叶是怎么被发现的？

_____

_____

5. 什么样的气候适合种茶？

_____

_____

6. 为什么杭州附近生产茶叶？

_____

_____

IX. 口头报告：地理 Oral Report: Geography

Step 1: Choose a country that interests you (for example: the USA, India, Egypt, Peru, etc.) Search online to gather some information about the geography of that country. The following table is to help you organize your presentation, or you can develop your own presentation outline.

国家	
地理位置 (geographic location) （在什么洲，靠近哪些 国家，是不是靠海…）	
地理情况 （东南西北部的 情况，山地、平原、 河流…）	
重要的城市或地区	
其他 （对农业的影响，有 名的旅游景点，特别 的情况…）	

Step 2: Make an oral presentation in class.

三・写作练习

Based on Activity IX, write about the geography of the country that you have selected. Your geography teacher happens to be a contributor to Wikipedia. He wants to submit a collective contribution under the title of "World Geography." Please check the accuracy of your information.

2.2 中国的地方菜系
Regional Cuisines in China

一·听力练习

 I. 连连线! **Match Them!**

In Audio Clip 2-2-1 you will hear definitions/explanations of different Chinese dishes. Match these definitions/explanations with the name of dishes in Column B. Enter the corresponding numbers and definitions/explanations in Column A.

A栏：请把你听到的写下来	B栏：菜名
	涮羊肉
	西湖醋鱼
	蔬菜牛肉
	海鲜面
	松鼠鱼
	酸辣汤
	春卷
	鸡肉炒饭
	饺子
	月饼

II. 对话理解 Dialogue Comprehension

Listen to the recording of the Lesson 2.2 Dialogue first, and then answer the True/False questions in Audio Clip 2-2-2.

	1	2	3	4
对				
错				

III. 课文理解 Text Comprehension

Listen to the recording of the Lesson 2.2 Text first, and then answer the True/False questions in Audio Clip 2-2-3.

	1	2	3	4
对				
错				

IV. 回答问题 Answer the Questions

Listen carefully to the questions in Audio Clip 2-2-4 and answer them according to your own situation. Record your answers on an audio recorder. You have 20 seconds to record your answers. If you do not have a recording device, arrange with your teacher to leave him/her a voicemail or write down your answers below in pinyin or characters.

1. _____

2. _____

3. _____

4. _____

5. _____

6. _____

V. 听短文 Listen to the Short Passages

Audio Clip 2-2-5 includes three short passages. Each selection is followed by two or three questions based on its content. After listening to each passage, answer the questions in Chinese. Each passage will be read twice.

Passage 1

1. 要是你打算参加国际食品节，你要去哪儿？

_____

2. 这个食品节是谁办的？

_____

3. 这个食品节将在什么时候办？

_____

Passage 2

1. 参加中国人的酒席时，最重要的客人一般坐在什么地方？

_____

2. 在中国的酒席上，上菜的次序 (cìxù, order) 是什么？

_____

3. 中国的酒席上，冷菜和热菜一般要有几个？

_____

4. 在中国参加酒席，你怎么知道酒席快要结束了？

_____

Passage 3

1. 这篇文章里说，小饭馆儿跟大饭店有什么不同？

_____

_____

2. 在中国的高级饭店，服务费一般是多少？

_____

_____

3. 听了这篇文章以后，你觉得去小饭馆儿的好处是什么？

_____

_____

_____

 VI. 中国文化短文 **A Short Text on Chinese Culture**

In Audio Clip 2-2-6 a student is giving a presentation based on a famous Chinese holiday tradition. After listening to the presentation, decide based on its content whether each statement is true or false. The presentation will be played twice. You can take notes while listening.

Below is a word bank that may help you understand the presentation better.

腊八粥	là bā zhōu	La Ba porridge	供佛	gòngfó	to give offerings to the Buddha
佛祖	fózǔ	the Buddha			
得道	dédào	become enlightened	雍和宫	Yōnghégōng	the Yonghe Buddhist Temple
释迦牟尼	Shìjiāmóní	Sakyamuni Buddha	皇室	huángshì	the royal family
化缘	huàyuán	receive alms	喇嘛	lǎma	Lama
熬	áo	boil	铜	tóng	copper

Notes:

对不对?

	对	错
1. The Chinese usually eat "La Ba Zhou" on December 8th.		
2. La Ba porridge is a food made in memory of the Buddha.		
3. La Ba porridge is made of rice and beans.		
4. In the Qing Dynasty, La Ba porridge was an important holiday food for commoners but not for the royal family and court officials.		

二 · 综合语言练习

Ⅰ. 用汉语怎么说? How do you say it in Chinese?

If a word or a phrase is provided, try to use it in your sentence.

1. A food connoisseur is knowledgeable about what and how to eat. (对···有研究)

_____

2. The Hui ethnic group is one of the major ethnic groups in China. Its population is about 100 million. (之一)

_____

3. In the Tang Dynasty, some merchants from Persia and Central Asia came to China for business. They are the ancestors of the Hui ethnic group.

_____

4. "Lamb dipped in hot soup" is a specialty of the Mongolian ethnic group.

_____

5. Different ethnic groups in China have lived together for hundreds of years. Their eating habits influence one another.

_____

6. The geographic environment and climate influence agriculture and diet.

_____

7. Generally speaking, Chinese food is divided into eight major cuisines. （一般来说）

_____

8. The characteristics of Chinese cuisines are "sweet in the south, salty in the north, spicy in the east, and sour in the west."

_____

9. Some people like lightly-flavored food and some like strongly-flavored food.

_____

10. A lot of fresh vegetables and seafood are used in Cantonese dishes.

_____

II. 结对活动：回族 Pair Activity: The Hui Ethnic Group

Based on the Lesson 2.2 Dialogue, fill out the information chart below about the Hui ethnic group. After you have finished, compare notes with your partner.

中国的少数民族之一：回族

人口	
居住地	
宗教 (religion)	
历史	
饮食习惯	

III. 涮羊肉 All About "Mongolian Hot Pot"

Based on the Dialogue in Lesson 2.2, choose the statements that contain accurate information on "Mongolian Hot Pot" (Lamb Dipped in Hot Soup).

1. 涮羊肉是唐朝的时候，波斯商人带到中国来的。	
2. 现在，中国许多民族都喜欢吃涮羊肉。	
3. 元朝的时候，蒙古军队开始吃涮羊肉。	
4. 涮羊肉是中国回族的特色菜。	
5. 做涮羊肉很快，也比较容易。	
6. 涮羊肉就是把羊肉切成一片一片的，在水里涮一下就吃。	
7. 因为蒙古军队觉得涮羊肉的味道很好，后来就有了涮羊肉这道菜。	
8. 吃涮羊肉的时候，应该同时喝十二味香茶。	

IV. 小组活动 Group Activity: Major Chinese Cuisines

Step 1: Form a group of three or four. Based on the Lesson 2.2 Text, take turns answering the following questions.

1. 中国各地的饮食为什么不太一样？

_____

_____

2. 中国人的主食是什么？

_____

_____

3. 中国菜被分成几个主要菜系？

_____

_____

4. 中国各地的菜有什么特点？

_____

_____

5. 请介绍一下中国江南地区的菜。

_____

_____

6. 请介绍一下中国北部和东北的菜。

_____

_____

7. 请介绍一下中国西部的菜。

_____

_____

8. 请介绍一下四川和湖南的菜。

_____

_____

9. 请介绍一下广东菜。

_____

_____

10. 为什么广东人是最敢吃的？

_____

_____

Step 2: After the questions are answered, each group selects a topic from the list below and prepares a one-minute presentation.

中国的地理和饮食	广东菜的特点	中国各地菜的特点	中国北方菜的特点	上海菜的特点

Step 3: Make an oral presentation in class.

V. 全班活动：谁是专家？ **Mixer Activity: Who is the expert?**

Step 1: Think about three things that you are knowledgeable about. Write them down in the order of most knowledgeable to least knowledgeable. You will use the following list when interviewed by other students.

非常有研究	比较有研究	有一点儿研究

Step 2: Circulate around the classroom to interview three students and find out what they are knowledgeable about. Take notes during your interviews.

Model: 你： 你对什么非常有研究？ or

你对什么比较有研究？ or

你对什么有一点儿研究？

你同学： 我对流行音乐非常有研究。

	非常有研究	比较有研究	有一点儿研究
同学一			
同学二			
同学三			

Step 3: If you find two students are knowledgeable about the same thing, introduce them to each other.

Model: 你： A，这是B，他对流行音乐比较有研究。

VI. 小组活动：哪个店家比较好？ Group Activity: A Business Review

Step 1: Form a group of three or four. Choose a business (restaurant, shop, theatre, park…) that all of you have been to. Everyone makes a comment about the business by using 从···看. Make sure that your comments do not overlap. After everyone has spoken, prepare a one-minute review of the business.

Model: A: 从服务看，大华超市不能算太好。

B: 从商品看，大华超市的品种非常多。

C: 从停车看，大华超市的停车场很大。

D: 从商店大小看，大华超市比较小。

Step 2: Select one student as the group representative. Make a presentation of the business review in class.

VII. 结对活动：惯例 Pair Activity: What is the general practice?

Step 1: You are going to talk about general practices in your country. Choose one topic from the following list that both you and your partner have something to say about.

运动	饮食	娱乐	交通	旅游	社会活动	住房	教育

Step 2: Think about what the general practices are as far as that topic is concerned. Make two comments on the topic by using 一般来说. Take turns telling each other what you consider to be a common practice. When one partner speaks, the other can take notes. After you have finished, review each other's notes to ensure accuracy.

Model: Suppose you have selected 娱乐.

一般来说，美国人喜欢看电视。

题目：	
1.	2.
3.	4.

Step 3: Switch partners with another pair. Tell the new partner what general practices you and your old partner thought of for your topic.

VIII. 小对话 Mini-Dialogue

A	B
You start first. • Ask if B has been to the newly-opened Muslim (穆斯林, Mùsīlín) restaurant near your school. • Tell B you went there last Friday and had a very special meal. • Tell B you had the Mongolian Hot Pot. • Tell B you dipped sliced lamb into a boiling soup. • Tell B it was started by the Mongolian army in the Yuan Dynasty. The cook wanted to cook the lamb quickly and dipped the lamb in boiling water. It is really a very tasty dish.	**Your partner starts first.** • Tell A you haven't. Ask if A has been there. • Ask what A ate. • Ask A to describe the dish. • Tell A it sounds interesting. Ask if A knows about the history of this dish. • Tell A you'd like to try the dish some day.
Your partner starts first. • Ask if B ate the "Sweet and Sour Pork" and "Chicken Fried Noodles." • Ask why B didn't eat them. • Ask what is special about the Northern Cuisine in China. • Ask what B ate. • Tell B that you would like to go there someday. Ask for the address of the restaurant.	**You start first.** • Tell A you went to a Chinese restaurant last Saturday. • Tell A even though those two are among your favorites, you didn't eat them last Saturday. • Tell A you went to a different kind of Chinese restaurant. It was a Northern Cuisine restaurant (北方菜馆). • Tell A because Northerners in China eat wheat flour, the restaurant serves many kinds of noodles and dumplings. • Tell A you had pork, beef, and vegetable dumplings. They are all very delicious. • Tell A where the restaurant is.

IX. 口头报告：美味的菜系 Oral Report: A Tasty Cuisine

Step 1: Search online for one of the eight major cuisines of China or for one cuisine that really interests you (such as Greek, French, Italian, Indian, etc.). Take notes on what you have found and prepare an oral report in Chinese. The following table is to help you organize your presentation, but you can also develop your own presentation outline.

菜系的名字	
在什么地方	
地理、气候、农业出产	
历史	
菜系里有名的菜	
菜的特点	
菜的味道	
其他：（比如：有名的饭店，烹调的过程…）	

Step 2: Make an oral presentation in class.

三·写作练习

Based on Activity VIII, write a short description (150-200 characters) of the cuisine you chose. It is helpful to give specific examples of the signature dishes of the cuisine. Try to describe, in some detail, the ingredients and the taste of the dishes.

2.3 饮食全球化
The Globalization of Food

一·听力练习

 I. 连连线! **Match Them!**

Match the descriptions you hear in Audio Clip 2-3-1 with the terms in Column B. Enter the corresponding numbers and descriptions in Column A.

A 栏：请把你听到的写下来	B 栏：短语
	越来越相似
	特色食品
	饮食全球化
	饮食差别
	换换口味
	地地道道
	暴饮暴食
	种在当地，吃在当地。

II. 对话一理解 **Dialogue 1 Comprehension**

Listen to the recording of Dialogue 1 from Lesson 2.3 first, and then answer the True/False questions in Audio Clip 2-3-2.

	1	2	3	4
对				
错				

 III. 对话二理解 **Dialogue 2 Comprehension**

Listen to the recording of Dialogue 2 from Lesson 2.3 first, and then answer the True/False questions in Audio Clip 2-3-3.

	1	2	3	4
对				
错				

 IV. 回答问题 **Answer the Questions**

Answer the questions in this section based on your understanding of the Lesson 2.3 dialogues.

Directions: Listen carefully to the questions in Audio Clip 2-3-4 and record your answers on an audio recorder. You have 20 seconds to record your answers. If you do not have a recording device, arrange with your teacher to leave him/her a voicemail or write down your answers below in pinyin or characters.

1. _____

2. _____

3. _____

4. _____

5. _____

6. _____

V. 听短文 Listen to the Short Passages

Audio Clip 2-3-5 includes contains three short passages. Each passage is followed by a number of questions regarding its content. After listening to each passage, answer the questions in English. Each selection will be played twice.

Passage 1

1. 中国有几个菜系？

_____

_____

2. 为什么以前中国各地的菜系有那么明显（míngxiǎn, obvious）的特点？

_____

_____

3. 为什么现在在中国很难能吃到很地道的八大菜系的菜？

_____

_____

_____

Passage 2

1. 为什么肯德基派到中国的第一位经理觉得肯德基在中国赚不到钱？

_____

_____

2. 肯德基派到中国的第二位经理是怎么做市场调查的？

_____

_____

_____

3. 肯德基在北京开了第一家饭馆以后有什么样的成功？

_____

_____

<u>Passage 3</u>

1. 在中国，绿色食品还有别的什么名字？

_____

2. 中国的绿色食品的标志是什么形状 (xíngzhuàng, shape) 的？

_____

3. 这个标志上有什么？

_____

 VI. 中国文化短文 A Short Text on Chinese Culture

In Audio Clip 2-3-6 a student is giving a presentation based on a famous Chinese holiday tradition. After listening to the presentation, decide based on its content whether each statement is true or false. The presentation will be played twice. You can take notes while listening.

Below is a word bank that may help you understand the presentation better.

咬	yǎo	bite	发芽	fāyá	sprout
立春	lì chūn	Beginning of Spring	涵义	hányì	implication
春蒿	chūnhāo	spring wormwood	贫富贵贱	pín fù guì jiàn	rich or poor, noble or ordinary
黄韭	huángjiǔ	spring chives			

Notes:

对不对?

	对	错
1. Spring rolls are an everyday food in China.		
2. The custom of eating spring rolls began in the Ming Dynasty.		
3. In China, eating spring rolls symbolizes the arrival of the spring.		
4. On the day of *li chun*, the residents of Beijing used to give each other spring rolls as good wishes.		

二 · 综合语言练习

I. 用汉语怎么说? How do you say it in Chinese?

If a word or a phrase is provided, try to use it in your sentence.

1. No matter which country it is, what people eat has become more and more similar. (无论…都…)

_____

2. Even though different regions have a few local specialty foods, the majority of food is the same. (虽然…但是…)

_____

3. Some fast foods have become world foods.

_____

4. Every country's diet was determined by its agriculture. (由…决定)

_____

5. "Growing locally and eating locally" can help local agricultural production.

_____

6. It is a pity that we live in a small town and don't have opportunities to taste food from other countries. (可惜)

_____

7. I would like to have some authentic Korean food.

_____

8. Brazilian barbecue has beef, lamb, pork, and chicken. You can choose what you like to eat.

_____

9. When there is delicious food, he often eats excessively.

_____

10. The globalization of diet has made many people change their traditional diets.

_____

II. 结对活动： "种在当地，吃在当地" 的长处和短处 Pair Activity: The Pros and Cons of Growing and Eating Locally

Step 1: Based on Dialogue 1 in Lesson 2.3, list the advantages and disadvantages of "growing locally and eating locally."

种在当地，吃在当地的好处	种在当地，吃在当地的坏处

Step 2: In addition to the pros and cons of "growing locally and eating locally" mentioned in Dialogue 1, can you think of some other pros and cons? Discuss with your partner and add your ideas to the list above.

Step 3: As a class, compile a longer list of the pros and cons of "growing locally and eating locally."

III. 对不对？ True or False?

Based on Dialogue 2 in Lesson 2.3, decide whether the following statements are true or false.

	对	错
1. 大卫说星期五考完试以后，大家应该一起出去吃西餐。		
2. 学校的学生餐厅每天都有中餐。		
3. 学校旁边有几家很地道的西餐店。		
4. 大卫觉得，快餐店不能算是地道的西餐店。		
5. 因为巴西烤肉的味道非常好，现在许多大城市都有巴西烤肉店。		
6. 巴西烤肉有各种各样的肉。		
7. 巴西烤肉店的盘子很小，所以大家一般要吃十盘。		
8. 在巴西烤肉店，服务员拿着肉串在饭店里走来走去。		
9. 在巴西烤肉店，无论你要吃多少肉都可以。		
10. 南美洲是全世界最早养牛的洲。		

IV. 小组活动 Group Activity: Help the Family Farm

Suppose you are volunteering at the non-governmental organization (NGO) "Green Village" (绿色家园). This NGO helps farmers in various countries to keep their farms and their traditional ways of farming and living. Recently Green Village received an email from a family-run farm in China asking for help.

Step 1: Read the email from China.

Send	Reply	Reply All	Forward	Print	Delete

绿色家园的朋友们：你们好！

我叫王前，是中国山东省一个高中的学生。我们家祖祖辈辈都是农民。十年以前，我家办了一个农场："青山农场"。我的爷爷、奶奶、爸爸、妈妈、姐姐都在农场工作，我每天从学校回来以后，也在农场工作。我们主要种玉米和蔬菜，爷爷还种了二十五棵苹果树，奶奶养了一百多只鸡。每个周末，我们去城里的农夫 (nóngfū, farmer) 市场，爸爸妈妈负责卖蔬菜水果，我和姐姐负责卖烤玉米和茶叶蛋。经过全家人的努力，我们的生活过得不错。

可是，最近城里新开了一个很大的超市。超市里的商品五花八门，不但有中国生产的食品，还有世界各国生产的食品。超市的门口还开了一个西式快餐店，那里卖汉堡、炸鸡、三明治什么的。不少年轻人和小孩子都喜欢去快餐店吃快餐，因为电视里常常放快餐店的广告。现在来我这儿买烤玉米和茶叶蛋的人多半是老年人，而且越来越少。以前我一个周末可以卖两百多个玉米和一百多个鸡蛋，现在只能卖一百多个玉米，六七十个鸡蛋了。爸爸妈妈说，来买蔬菜水果的人也比以前少了，因为不少人觉得去超市买东西比去农夫市场方便。那儿什么都有，买菜啊、肉啊、米啊、面啊都在一个地方，不用去几个地方了。

自从开了超市以来，我们的生活受到不少影响。因为家里的收入 (shōurù, income) 一直在减少，前两天，爸爸妈妈在讨论是不是应该把家庭农场关了。这样，他们俩可以去城里找工作，多挣一点儿钱。爷爷奶奶听了很难过，他们都非常喜欢这个农场，种果树养鸡是他们的生活。爷爷说，农场没有了，他的生活也就没有意思了。爸爸妈妈还担心能不能找到工作，要是他们在城里找不到工作的话，就没有钱送我去上大学了。

我希望我们的青山农场能办下去，我们全家一定会努力工作。可是我想了半天，也想不出什么跟超市竞争的好办法。今天给你们写信，就是希望你们能给我一些建议。

非常感谢你们的帮助！

王前

Step 2: Divide the class into three groups. Each group works on the assigned task(s).

<u>Group 1:</u>

Brainstorm strategies for Wang's family to keep the "Green Mountain Farm." Write your suggestions in the space below.

1.	
2.	
3.	
4.	
5.	
6.	
7.	
8.	

<u>Group 2:</u>

1. Brainstorm public platforms where the "Green Mountain Farm" can advocate "growing locally and eating locally."
2. Write several slogans that support "growing locally and eating locally."

Public platforms	

Slogans that support "growing locally and eating locally"

Group 3:

Prepare a few recipes for the products produced at the "Green Mountain Farm." The purpose is to show potential customers that they can prepare simple and nutritious meals with locally produced food.

Recipe 1
Recipe 2
Recipe 3

Recipe 4

Step 3: Each group presents its completed task(s) in class.

V. 全班活动：小镇的相同之处 Mixer Activity: Similarities among Small Towns

Step 1: Your teacher will assign you a card. First, study the card assigned to you and see if you know the expressions necessary to complete the task written on your card. You can write down your questions in the space provided. Your questions need to contain 无论…都…

Model:　问题：无论在哪个小镇都能吃到蔬菜吗？
　　　　回答：是的 or 不一定。

1	2
Find at least one person who believes that you can eat fruits in every small town.	Find at least one person who believes that you can eat pizza in every small town.
Find at least one person who believes that you can watch TV cooking programs in every small town.	Find at least one person who believes that there is a Chinese restaurant in every small town.
Find at least one person who believes that you can eat pizza in every small town.	Find at least one person who believes that you can take a bus in every small town.

3	4
Find at least one person who believes that there is a supermarket in every small town.	Find at least one person who believes that you can eat hamburgers in every small town.
Find at least one person who believes that you can take a bus in every small town.	Find at least one person who believes that there is an Italian restaurant in every small town.
Find at least one person who believes that there is a place you can buy tea in every small town.	Find at least one person who believes that you can eat pizza in every small town.
5	**6**
Find at least one person who believes that you can get fresh seafood in every small town.	Find at least one person who believes that there is a place you can buy tea in every small town.
Find at least one person who believes that there is a museum in every small town.	Find at least one person who believes that there is a baseball team in every small town.
Find at least one person who believes that there is a place you can buy tea in every small town.	Find at least one person who believes that you can take a bus in every small town.

Step 2: Walk around the classroom and interview as many classmates as you can. Make sure that you speak only in Chinese. Once you have finished the tasks, you can stop the interviews.

VI. 小对话：大城市和小城镇 Role Play: Large Cities vs. Small Towns

A	B
Your friend is thinking about relocating to a big city after high school. You have always loved your life in a small town. Try to let your friend know there are many advantages to living in a small town, such as housing, traffic, personal relations… (try to use 对…有好处).	You are thinking about relocating to a big city after finishing high school. Even though you have always lived in a small town, you believe there are many advantages to living in a big city, such as jobs, social life, opportunities, cultural activities… (try to use 对…有好处).
You are planning to attend college in a large city. In your opinion, there are many advantages to living in a large city. Tell your friend these advantages, such as entertainment, restaurants, night life, sport events… (try to use 对…有好处).	Your friend is planning to attend college in a large city. You know your friend lacks self control and may have too much fun at the cost of his/her college education. You feel your friend will benefit more from a university located in a small town (try to use 对…有好处).

VII. 全班活动：那是什么食品? Mixer Activity: Name that special food!

Your school is going to organize an "International Day" for students, teachers, parents, and community members. One of the activities is to prepare food from all over the world. In order to get as many ideas as possible about what food to prepare, you will participate in a survey.

Step 1: Read the questions. If you feel food items from that country should be prepared, think of one dish and write its name in the survey form. (You need to think of at least four dishes.)

Model:　问题：　　　我们应该准备日本食品吗?

　　　　　你的回答：(if you agree) 饭团

在国际日	你	同学一	同学二
我们应该准备中国食品吗?			
我们应该准备意大利食品吗?			
我们应该准备德国食品吗?			
我们应该准备韩国食品吗?			
我们应该准备巴西食品吗?			

我们应该准备俄国食品吗？			
我们应该准备法国食品吗？			
我们应该准备日本食品吗？			
我们应该准备美国食品吗？			
我们应该准备墨西哥食品吗？			

Step 2: Go around the classroom and interview two students, recording their answers in the worksheet above. When you are being interviewed, you need to use 尤其 in your answers.

Model: 问题：我们应该准备中国食品吗？

你： 是的，尤其应该准备饺子。or 我不了解中国食品。

Step 3: Form a group of three or four. Compare your survey results with the group. The goal is to have at least one special dish from each country listed in the worksheet above.

VIII. 结对活动：生词宾果 Pair Activity: Word Bingo

Step 1: Randomly select 16 words from the following word bank to fill your bingo grid. Make sure you know what the words mean in English.

Word Bank

冷冻	暴吃	好处	简单	能源	种
相似	全球化	品尝	南美洲	运	当地
养牛	肉串	无论	选择	差别	尤其

Step 2: Pair up with a classmate. Take turns calling out one word at a time. When it is your partner's turn to call out a word, listen carefully. If you have that word in your bingo grid, tell your partner "我有" and say the English meaning of the word before crossing it out. Whoever crosses out four words in a row (horizontally, vertically, or diagonally) wins the game.

三·写作练习

Write an essay (approximately 150-200 Chinese characters) about typical meals at your home.

题目：我家的饮食

You essay should:

1. Describe the typical meals your family has (breakfast, lunch, and dinner)
2. Discuss whether your family's meals are influenced by any ethnic cuisines (Mexican, Chinese, Italian…)
3. State your opinion on the advantages and disadvantages of ethnic influences. Support your opinion with facts.
4. Summarize the main characteristics of your family meals in a short paragraph.

2.4 "绿色食品"和"健康食品"
"Green Food" and "Health Food"

一·听力练习

 I. 连连线! Match Them!

Match the definitions you hear in Audio Clip 2-4-1 with the words and phrases in Column B. Enter the corresponding numbers and phrases in Column A.

A栏：请把你听到的写下来	B栏：短语
	健康食品
	天然食品
	有机食品
	绿色食品
	垃圾 (lājī, junk) 食品
	素食品
	油炸食品
	特色食品
	保健食品
	减肥食品

II. 对话一理解 Dialogue 1 Comprehension

Listen to the recording of Dialogue 1 from Lesson 2.4 first, and then answer the True/False questions in Audio Clip 2-4-2.

	1	2	3
对			
错			

 III. 对话二理解 Dialogue 2 Comprehension

Listen to the recording of Dialogue 2 from Lesson 2.4 first, and then answer the True/False questions in Audio Clip 2-4-3.

	1	2	3	4
对				
错				

 IV. 回答问题 Answer the Questions

Listen carefully to the questions in Audio Clip 2-4-4 and answer them according to your own situation. Record your answers on an audio recorder. You have 20 seconds to record your answers. If you do not have a recording device, arrange with your teacher to leave him/her a voicemail or write down your answers below in pinyin or characters.

1. _____

2. _____

3. _____

4. _____

5. _____

6. _____

V. 听短文 Listen to the Short Passages

Audio Clip 2-4-5 includes three short passages. Each selection is followed by two or three questions based on its content. After listening to each passage, answer the questions in Chinese. Each passage will be read twice.

Passage 1

1. 根据美国农业部的"我的盘子"(MyPlate)，我们每天吃得最多的应该是什么？

_____

_____

2. 要有健康的身体，除了注意饮食以外，每天应该运动多长时间？

_____

_____

3. 为了健康，是不是有些食物不应该吃？

_____

_____

Passage 2

1. 中国人的饮食中，吃得最多的是什么？

_____

_____

2. 请说出三种中国传统的点心和小吃？

_____

_____

3. 为什么以前中国人吃水果吃得不太多？

_____

_____

Passage 3

1. 为什么很多高中生不是很胖就是很瘦？

_____

_____

2. 中国老师对提高高中生的健康有什么建议？

_____

_____

 VI. 中国文化短文 A Short Text on Chinese Culture

In Audio Clip 2-4-6 a student is giving a presentation based on a famous Chinese holiday tradition. After listening to the presentation, decide whether each statement based on the content is true or false. The presentation will be played twice. You can take notes while listening.

Below is a word bank that may help you understand the presentation better.

俗语	súyǔ	common saying	子时	zǐshí	midnight
元宝	yuánbǎo	ingots made of silver or gold	煮	zhǔ	boil
招	zhāo	hail	更岁交子	gēng suì jiāo zǐ the new year replaces the old at midnight on New Year's Eve	
明清	míngqing	Ming and Qing Dynasties	时刻	shíkè	moment
盛行	shèngxíng	popular	圆圆满满	yuányuánmǎnmǎn	fulfilling

Notes:

对不对？

	对	错
1. The Chinese eat dumplings on Chinese New Year's Eve because they symbolize prosperity.		
2. The Chinese usually wrap some dumplings at midnight on New Year's Eve for good luck.		
3. In China, eating dumplings on New Year's Eve has the meaning of "the changing of the year," because the Chinese word for dumplings, *jiaozi*, is a homonym of *jiaozi*, meaning midnight passes.		
4. In the past, people wrapped gold ingots inside dumplings eaten on New Year's Eve.		

二 · 综合语言练习

l. 用汉语怎么说？ How do you say it in Chinese?

If a word or a phrase is provided, try to use it in your sentence.

1. Many foods have the "green food" label.

_____

2. What is the difference between "natural food" and "organic food"？（差别）

_____

3. Too many food labels make people confused.（糊里糊涂）

_____

4. Is food without pollution "green food"？

_____

5. "Organic food" means no chemicals are used during growing.

_____

6. Food that has not been processed is "natural food."

_____

7. Food that has been processed only lightly is also "natural food."

_____

8. Many food labels only tell us what happened when the food was growing.

_____

II. 这些标志是什么意思？ **What does the label mean?**

Based on the Lesson 2.4 dialogues, choose the best definition from the choices provided.

1. 绿色食品的意思是：
   (A) 绿颜色的食品，像青菜、绿葡萄、绿苹果什么的。
   (B) 没有污染的食品。
   (C) 没有化学品的食品。
   (D) 加过工的食品。

2. 有机食品的意思是：
   (A) 有机会吃到的食品。
   (B) 没有加过工的食品。
   (C) 生产这种食品的时候，不用化学品。
   (D) 没有污染的蔬菜和水果。

3. 天然食品的意思是：
   (A) 没经过或者只经过很少加工的食品。
   (B) 不用化学品的食品。
   (C) 大家天天吃的食品。
   (D) 对健康有好处的食品。

4. 健康食品的意思是：
   (A) 天然食品、有机食品和绿色食品。
   (B) 又好吃又有营养的食品。
   (C) 去健身房锻炼身体以前要吃的食品。
   (D) 对健康有好处的食品。

III. 对不对？ True or False?

Based on the Lesson 2.4 dialogues, decide whether the following statements are true or false.

	对	错
1. 健康食品都是天然的，没有化学品。		
2. 绿色食品和健康食品的意思是一样的。		
3. 有机食品在生产的时候，没有用过化学品。		
4. 像薯片、饼干、巧克力这样的食品一定不是绿色食品。		
5. 食品不都是天然生长的，有些食品是用化学品制造的。		
6. 有机食品在生产和加工的时候，没有受到污染。		
7. 天然食品和有机食品的意思差不多，都是没有经过加工的食品。		
8. 食品的标志太多，容易让人糊里糊涂。		
9. 吃"绿色食品"比较安全。		
10. 不管是什么食品，都可能对人的健康有好处或者坏处。		

IV. 结对活动：另一种意见 Pair Activity: A Second Opinion

Step 1: Work as individuals. Complete the following worksheet based on your own opinions.

（ ）是最好看的电影。	同意	不同意
（ ）是最美丽的旅游点。	同意	不同意
（ ）是最有意思的工作。	同意	不同意
（ ）是又有营养又好吃的食品。	同意	不同意
（ ）是最容易学习的课程。	同意	不同意
（ ）是大家最喜欢上网做的事。	同意	不同意

Step 2: Follow the model to exchange your opinions. Listen to your partner carefully. If both of you have the same answers, circle 同意 on the worksheet. If you have different answers, circle 不同意. Make sure to use 不见得 if you have a different opinion from your partner.

Model:　你同学：　哈里波特是最好看的电影。

　　　　　你：　　　我同意。

　　　　　　　　　　or

　　　　　你：　　　哈里波特不见得是最好看的电影。

Step 3: Report in class whether there are more things you agree or disagree about.

V.　小组活动：举三个例子 Group Activity: Name Three Examples

Step 1: Divide the class into groups of three. One group member acts as the game host and the other two as Contestant A and Contestant B.

Step 2: The host will read out the incomplete sentences one at a time. The contestants will take turns completing the sentences by adding "像 + three examples." If the contestant completes a sentence correctly, s/he will receive one point. Otherwise, s/he will receive zero points. The contestant with the higher total score wins the game.

Model:

Host:	天然食品非常多…	Host:	天然食品非常多…
Contestant:	像鱼、肉、蔬菜。	Contestant:	鱼、肉、蔬菜。
Host:	对，得一分。	Host:	得零分。

Score Sheet

	A	B
1. 不少食品已经全球化了，		
2. 高中生有不少必修课，		
3. 美国学生喜欢这些体育活动，		
4. 中国有不少大城市，		
5. 这些电影都非常有意思，		

6. 上网可以做许多不同的事，		
7. 多吃这些食品对健康没有好处，		
8. 在大城市里有各国的饭店，		
9. 出去旅行的时候，应该带这些东西，		
10. 在超市里可以买到各种各样的食品，		
总分：		

VI. 结对活动 Pair Activity: Mini-Dialogue

A	B
You start: • Ask where B usually buys food. • Ask why B likes organic food. • Agree with B. Tell B you usually shop for "green food" at a supermarket. • Tell B not all organic food is necessarily green food. Green food means the food is not polluted. Therefore, if an organic food is polluted, it can't be called "green food".	**Your partner starts:** • Tell A you usually buy food at a farmer's market, because some farmers sell organic food. • Tell A organic food is better for your health, because during its production, no chemicals are used. • Ask A if all organic food is green food. • Tell A sometimes it is hard to know what all the different food labels mean.
Your partner starts: • Tell B no one in your family likes to cook, so you eat a lot of processed food, such as pizza, frozen dinners, and fast food. • Tell B you are interested, but no one in your family is able to teach you. • Ask what B's parents usually cook. • Ask B if it is difficult to cook from scratch. • Tell B you would be delighted to go on Saturday. Eating less processed food will be good for your health.	**You start:** • Ask who usually cooks in A's family. • Ask if A is interested in learning how to cook. • Tell A your parents are both good cooks and they would be happy to teach A. • Tell A your parents like to cook from scratch (天然食品). • Tell A some food is easy to cook. Invite A to your house for a cooking lesson on Saturday.

VII. 小组活动：买食品的建议 Group Activity: Suggestions for Buying Food

Step 1: Divide the class into groups of three or four. Food safety is important to consumers. In small groups, brainstorm what measures you can take to ensure you are buying good quality and safe foods. Take notes in the space provided below.

用以下的方法可以保证 (guarantee) 买来的食品是安全的：
1.
2.
3.
4.
5.
6.
7.
8.
9.
10.

Step 2: Groups take turns reporting their suggestions in class. Listen carefully. If other groups have suggestions that are different from your group's suggestions, add them to the list above. At the end of the discussion, count how many items are on your list. Keep the list for Activity VIII.

VIII. 这些建议怎么样？ Are these good suggestions?

This is a blog post on a website:

现在越来越多的人开始注意饮食和健康的关系。要健康，不但要运动，还要注意饮食。可是有时候，因为食品有问题，结果不少人吃了以后就生病了。为了大家的健康，我建议在买食品的时候，大家应该注意以下的情况：

一、先看食品的包装 (wrapping)袋。如果包装袋坏了，不干净，或者看上去很旧，最好不要买。

二、看食品的生产日期和保质期。如果食品是很久以前生产的，或者保质期马上要到期了，最好不要买。

三、有些食品没有生产商、生产地、和生产日期，这样的食品也不应该买。

四、看食品有没有QS的标志，QS是英文 Quality Safety （质量安全）。不少食品上都有这个标志，像大米、面、饼干、饮料、茶叶等等。

五、最好去比较大比较干净的超市和食品店买食品。不要在路边乱买食品。

六、在买新鲜食品的时候，必须注意食品是不是新鲜。

如果大家有别的好建议，请上载到网上来。谢谢！

Based on the blog post, answer the following questions in Chinese:

1. Why did the blogger make these suggestions?

_____

_____

2. What did the blogger say about food packaging?

_____

_____

3. What information can you get by looking at the food labels?

_____

_____

4. Where is a good place to shop for food?

_____

_____

5. Compare the blog post with the list you compiled in Activity VII. Did the blogger add anything to your list?

_____

_____

三・写作练习

Pick one category of food from the following list and write an essay (100-150 characters) about it.

有机食品	绿色食品	健康食品	天然食品	垃圾食品
减肥食品	美容 (beauty)食品	旅行食品	回族食品	方便食品

In your essay, you should include:

1. A definition of the food category.
2. A few examples from this category.
3. The pros and cons of consuming such food.
4. Personal likes or dislikes of such food (be sure to explain the reasons).
5. Other information or feelings you have about the food.

2.5   中国的饮食文化
China's Food Culture

一·听力练习

 I. 连连线! Match Them!

Match the words and phrases you hear in Audio Clip 2-5-1 with the definitions in Column B. Enter the corresponding numbers and phrases in Column A.

A 栏： 请把你听到的写下来	B 栏： 短语的意思
	这句话的意思是，对老百姓来说，吃饭是他们生活中最重要的事。
	这个短语是说做饭做得怎么样。
	这个短语说的是在饮食上的风俗习惯。
	这个短语的意思是一个国家或者文化在历史上有什么样的情况。
	这个词是指一个人很喜欢招待客人。
	这是去别人家访问的人。
	这是在自己家里招待别人的人。
	这个短语的意思是做了一件事马上就有结果。

II. 对话一理解 Dialogue 1 Comprehension

Listen to the recording of Dialogue 1 from Lesson 2.5 first, and then answer the True/False questions in Audio Clip 2-5-2.

	1	2	3	4
对				
错				

III. 对话二理解 **Dialogue 2 Comprehension**

Listen to the recording of Dialogue 2 from Lesson 2.5 first, and then answer the True/False questions in Audio Clip 2-5-3.

	1	2	3	4
对				
错				

 IV. 回答问题 **Answer the Questions**

Listen carefully to the questions in Audio Clip 2-5-4 and answer them according to your own situation. Record your answers on an audio recorder. You have 20 seconds to record your answers. If you do not have a recording device, arrange with your teacher to leave him/her a voicemail or write down your answers below in pinyin or characters.

1. _____

2. _____

3. _____

4. _____

5. _____

6. _____

V. 听短文 **Listen to the Short Passages**

Audio Clip 2-5-5 includes three short passages. Each passage is followed by two to four questions based on the content. After listening to each passage, answer the questions in Chinese. Each passage will be read twice.

Passage 1

Answer the following questions:

1. 要是你招待客人，给客人一杯茶，你要注意什么？

_____

2. 要是主人给你茶的时候，你非常渴，能不能把茶喝完？

_____

3. 要是你是客人，主人问你还要不要再喝一点儿茶，你应该说什么？

_____

Passage 2

True or False:

	对	错
1. 在中国，要是家里有客人来，主人一定要留客人吃饭。		
2. 主人第一次说请客人留下来吃饭的时候，客人应该马上说，好啊，谢谢！		
3. 如果客人真的没打算在主人家吃饭，应该在去主人家以前告诉主人。		

Passage 3

Answer the following questions:

1. 这篇文章说，中国人见面的时候最常常说的话是什么？

_____

2. 在汉语里，要是一件事非常有名，中国人会说什么？

_____

3. 在汉语里，"能吃苦"是什么意思？

_____

4. 如果大家说一本小说"味同嚼蜡"，意思是什么？

_____

VI. 中国文化短文 A Short Text on Chinese Culture

In Audio Clip 2-5-6 a student is giving a presentation based on a famous Chinese legend. After listening to the presentation, decide based on its content whether each statement is true or false. The presentation will be played twice. You can take notes while listening.

Below is a word bank that may help you understand the presentation better.

枣	zǎo	dates	打渔	dǎyú	go fishing
栗子	lìzǐ	chestnuts	妻子	qīzǐ	wife
夫妇	fūfù	a married couple	干枣	gānzǎo	dried dates
祝福	zhùfú	blessing	暴风雨	bàofēngyǔ	severe thunderstorm
早立子	zǎo lìzǐ	to have a son soon	靠着	kàozhe	rely on
陡	Dǒu	a surname	陡氏	Dǒushì	the Dous
丈夫	zhàngfū	husband	祝愿	zhùyuàn	wish

Notes:

对不对？

	对	错
1. In Mandarin, the words for dates and chestnuts are homophones of the words for "early" and "give birth to a son."		
2. Dates and chestnuts are common wedding gifts in China.		
3. The custom of giving dates and chestnuts to newlyweds has to do with the lost son of the Dou family.		
4. Mr. Dou survived on only a bag of dried dates when he was stranded on a small boat.		
5. Later on, the Chinese believed that the bag of dried dates helped the Dous to give birth to a son.		

二·综合语言练习

I. 用汉语怎么说？ How do you say it in Chinese?

If a word or a phrase is provided, try to use it in your sentence.

1. Eating is not only for getting full, but also for cultivating interpersonal feelings. （不但…而且…）

_____

_____

2. Hospitality is one of the Chinese cultural traditions. （之一）

_____

_____

3. Chinese people like to cook a lot of food for guests, ask guests to eat more, and (moreover) put food into guests' bowls. （并且）

_____

_____

4. Chinese people indeed like to eat together with friends and family. （的确）

_____

_____

5. Chinese people always feel that the most important thing in life is eating. （总是）

_____

_____

6. When cooking, Chinese people pay attention to a dish's color, smell, and taste.

_____

_____

7. According to Chinese tradition, we should eat different types of food in different seasons. （根据）

_____

_____

8. Chinese people divide foods into hot types, neutral types and cool types. （分成）

_____

_____

II. 对不对？ True or False?

Based on the Lesson 2.5 dialogues, decide whether the following statements are true or false.

	对	错
1. 一个国家的饮食是由农业决定的，怎么吃是由文化传统决定的。		
2. 中国人觉得吃饭不是为了吃饱，而是为了培养感情。		
3. 中国人很好客。他们请客人吃饭的时候，常常给客人夹菜。		
4. 在给客人夹菜的时候，中国人会先问客人吃饱没吃饱。		

5. 汤姆特别喜欢别人给他夹菜，所以非常喜欢跟中国人出去吃饭。		
6. 中国人吃熟的和热的食品。		
7. 中国人做菜的时候，喜欢在菜里放一些颜色。		
8. 因为有的东西不好吃，所以中国人做菜的时候放很多香料。		
9. 中国人把食物分成热性、中性和凉性。		
10. 中国人觉得，要是一个人吃很多辣的东西，就会长痘子。		

III. 结对练习：食文化 Pair Activity: Food as a Cultural Practice

Pair up with a partner. First, read Dialogue 1 from Lesson 2.5 carefully and pay attention to how each person participated in the discussion. Afterwards complete the following dialogue using the suggestions provided.

学生一：	学生二：
大卫说，一个国家吃什么可能由农业决定，可是怎么吃常常是由文化传统决定的。你同意吗？	(Respond to the question and elaborate your point using examples)
(Respond to the question and elaborate your point using examples)	我听很多人说，中国人喜欢聚在一起吃饭，因为对他们来说，吃饭主要是为了培养人跟人的感情。
我知道中国人好客，希望让客人吃得饱，吃得好。可是我很不习惯中国人为客人夹菜的习惯。你对这样的习惯有什么看法？	(Respond to the question and elaborate your point using examples)
(Respond to the question and elaborate your point using examples)	总的来说，给客人夹菜是因为中国人很好客。你觉得呢？

IV. 课堂辩论：一个国家的饮食是由农业还是文化传统决定的？ **In-Class Debate: Is a country's diet determined by its agriculture or by its cultural traditions?**

Step 1: In Lesson 2.5 you read about David's opinion on the impact of tradition on food and diet. What are your thoughts on the issue? In the form below, jot down three arguments（论点）for each thesis. Your arguments can be either for or against the thesis. Use some examples to support your argument.

饮食习惯是由农业生产决定的。	饮食习惯是文化传统决定的。
论点一 　例子1 　例子2 　例子3 论点二 　例子1 　例子2 　例子3 论点三 　例子1 　例子2 　例子3	论点一 　例子1 　例子2 　例子3 论点二 　例子1 　例子2 　例子3 论点三 　例子1 　例子2 　例子3

Step 2: Wait for your teacher to assign you a group and a thesis.

Step 3: Work with your group to develop an opening statement for your debate.

Step 4: Choose one person to be your group's representative. This person will be giving the opening statement. Also, decide who will be helping the group by taking notes during the debate.

Step 5: Follow the basic team debate format.

V. 全班活动：国际菜谱 Mixer Activity: An International Cookbook

Step 1: Find a recipe for your favorite food and translate it into Chinese. Create a vocabulary list and illustration for your recipe. You can also include the approximate cost for making the food. Your entire recipe must fit onto an 8.5"x11" sheet of paper.

Step 2: Display your recipe in the area designated by your teacher.

Step 3: Once everybody has their recipe on display, read all of them carefully and select five recipes from the display. Fill out the form below as you read these recipes.

菜的名字	哪国菜	需要什么原料	要多少钱
1.			
2.			
3.			
4.			
5.			

Step 4: Form a small group of three or four people. In your group, tell each other which recipes you have selected and justify your selections.

VI. 中国人怎么养生？ How do the Chinese take care of their bodies?

Step 1: Read the following article carefully.

　　中国人相信"天人合一"，也就是说，自然和人的生活应该是和谐 (héxié, in harmony) 的。中国古人认为，为了健康，一个人应该根据一年四季的天气和气候做合适的活动，并且吃那个季节特有的的食物。如果这样生活，一个人就不会生病。这种对身体和自然的关系的看法，就是中国人说的"养生"。

　　清朝的人有"六养"、"四少"的养生方法。"六养"是说有六种东西可以帮助养生："流水的声音对耳有好处。绿色的草地对眼睛有好处。看书和思考问题可以帮助人的心。弹琴、写毛笔字可以帮助人的手。走路可以帮助人的脚。静坐休息对人的筋骨有好处。这是说人不但要做运动，比如爬山、散步什么的，而且要读书思考，保持心理的健康。

　　"四少"是"口中言少，心中事少，肚中食少，自然睡少"，这并不是说一个人要少说话，少担心，少吃饭和少睡觉，而是说做什么都要合适，不要太多，也不要不够。有人说，要是按照这"四少"生活，那就可以成神仙 (shénxiān, immortal) 了。

Step 2: Answer the questions based on the article.

1. 中国人觉得什么是养生？

_____

_____

2. 中国人说的"养生"，跟运动有什么关系？

_____

_____

3. 在中国人的养生里，"四少"是什么意思？

_____

_____

4. 中国人的养生方法表现了什么样的哲学？

_____

_____

三・写作练习

The Chinese believe that natural foods have therapeutic functions. Over the past three thousand years, they have developed a theory and practice of food therapy. Do online research on Chinese food therapy and write an essay (100-150 characters) introducing one of the dietary remedies.

2.6 第二单元复习
Review of Unit 2

一·成语练习

In Audio Clip 2-6-1 you will hear a number of Chinese idioms and proverbs that have been previously introduced. After each idiom/proverb, you will be given 10 seconds to record a definition or explanation. Record your answers on an audio recorder. If you do not have a recording device, you can write down your answers below in pinyin or Chinese characters.

Word Bank

立竿见影	家常便饭	粗茶淡饭	山珍海味
百川归海	苦尽甘来	丰衣足食	五味俱全

Model:

You will hear:	You will say:
望子成龙	这个成语的意思是父母都希望子女很成功。

Notes	Your definition

二·口头报告

Choose a topic and give an oral presentation in class.

Topic 1   中国农业与南北方的饮食差异

Topic 2   介绍一种地方菜（中国的或者别国的都可以）

Topic 3   饮食全球化好处和坏处

Topic 4   "种在当地，吃在当地"对贫困国家的影响

Topic 5   为了我们的环境，请吃绿色食品！

Topic 6   饮食对中国人生活的影响

After you have chosen the topic, please write an outline for your presentation. You can write the outline on a separate sheet of paper. If your teacher allows, you can also transfer the outline to an index card as a reminder for when you give the presentation.

Your presentation must meet the following criteria:

1. It must have a beginning, a middle, and an end.
2. It must include as much detail as possible.
3. It must last no longer than two minutes.

三·综合语言练习

l. 对话理解 Dialogue Comprehension

Based on the Lesson 2.6 Dialogue, answer the following questions in Chinese.

1. 为什么大家都说，香港是"美食天堂"？

_____

_____

2. 食文化在香港和在其他大城市有什么不同？

_____

_____

3. 香港的街头食品有什么特点？

_____

_____

4. 香港饭馆的名字特别多，有"茶楼"、"酒楼"、还有"茶餐厅"。这些饭馆有什么不同？

_____

_____

5. 这篇对话里谈到广东菜，上海菜，和山东菜。这些菜都有什么特点？

_____

_____

Ⅱ. 结对活动：我们去大理吧！ **Pair Activity: Let's go to Dali!**

Pair up with a partner. First, read Mingying's email in Lesson 2.6 carefully and pay attention to the description of Dali. Afterwards complete the following conversation.

学生一	学生二
明英在电邮里说没说什么时候去大理旅游最好？	
	明英谈没谈大理的地方饮食有什么特点？
听说大理的白族有一种习惯，就是请客人喝"三道茶"。你知道不知道这是一种什么茶？	
	听上去大理这么有意思，是个文化旅游的好地方。我们什么时候去大理看看？

III. 小组活动：哪个成语？ Group Activity: Name That Proverb!

Step 1: Form small groups of four and come up with definitions for the following proverbs or common sayings. Choose one person from your group to write the definitions down on a piece of paper. Make sure to write neatly and clearly, as later you will be swapping your definitions with another group.

Model: 种在当地，吃在当地：为了保护环境，大家要吃在这个地方生产的食品。

1. 读万卷书，行万里路
2. 少壮不努力，老大徒伤悲
3. 言必行，行必果
4. 有志者，事竟成
5. 种在当地，吃在当地
6. 种瓜得瓜，种豆得豆
7. 民以食为天
8. 好吃不过年饺子
9. 三人行，必有我师
10. 三天打渔，两天晒网
11. 严师出高徒
12. 青出于蓝，而胜于蓝

Step 2: Swap your group's definitions with another group in your class.

Step 3: Stay within your own group. Choose one person from your group to be the host of the game; the other three will be the competitors. The host will read the definitions out loud and keep score. Each correct answer earns 10 points. Each incorrect answer loses 10 points. The person with the most points at the end of the game wins.

Score Sheet

Questions:	1	2	3	4	5	6	7	8	9	10	11	12
Contestant 1 Name: _____												
Contestant 2 Name: _____												
Contestant 3 Name: _____												

IV. 全班活动：饮食、健康和环境 Mixer Survey: Food, Health, and the Environment

While browsing on the Internet, you stumbled upon a website where someone posted the following article.

Step 1: Choose three statements from the article that you disagree with and write down your reasons in the space provided.

我对饮食健康和环境保护的几个建议
1. 为了减少我们对环境的污染，保护我们的健康，我们一定要"种在当地，吃在当地"。
2. 为了"种在当地，吃在当地"，我们每个人都应该种一些菜，养几只鸡，在家里的院子里种几棵果树。
3. 我们的饮食，一定要按照季节来决定。春夏秋冬吃的东西不应该都一样。
4. 为了健康，最好不吃粮食，比如，米饭、面包、面条什么的。
5. 我们每天吃的东西里，一半应该是蔬菜和水果，另一半是肉、蛋、海鲜。
6. 我们吃的蔬菜水果和鸡鸭鱼肉都应该是新鲜的，不应该是冰箱冷冻的。
7. 无论是水果还是蔬菜，是肉类还是海鲜，都必须是绿色食品，因为绿色食品都对健康有好处。
8. 咖啡、茶、汽水等等饮料都对健康没有好处。而且，这些饮料都要从别的地方运到这里来。所以，我们不应该再喝咖啡、茶、和汽水。我们应该只喝水。

我不同意第 ＿＿＿，第 ＿＿＿，和第 ＿＿＿，因为

_____

_____

_____

_____

_____

_____

_____

_____

_____

Step 2: Walk around the classroom and interview your classmates, asking whether they agree with the statements in the online article. You may only ask each classmate one question at a time. Once you have found two classmates who selected the same statements as you did, you can stop interviewing. The student who stops interviewing first wins the game.

Model:　你：　　我觉得，"种在当地，吃在当地"不见得是一种保护环境和健康的好方法，因为… (state your own reasons)。你说呢？

　　　　　　你同学：我同意，因为 … (state your own reasons), or 我不同意。

V. 网上聊天室 Online Chat Room

You are in an online chat room. Type your questions and answers in Chinese.

网友一：我们老师让我们准备一个关于春节的演讲。我想讲为什么中国人春节的时候一定要吃饺子。我记得老师说过，吃饺子的意思是恭喜发财。可是为什么呢？谁知道？能不能帮我一下？

网友二：好像饺子的样子象以前中国人用的钱。

你：　　_____

　　　　_____

网友一：真有意思。听说中国的饮食文化里有很多这样的象征。

网友二：是啊。听说中国人结婚的时候，亲戚朋友常常用枣和栗子做成果盘送给他们，谁知道这是为什么？

网友二：没错儿。我去年在北京的时候，参观了首都博物馆。在那儿有一个老北京的结婚习俗展览。我看见婚礼的桌子上和床上都有枣和栗子。可是不知道为什么。

你：　＿＿＿＿＿＿＿＿＿＿＿＿＿＿＿＿＿＿＿＿＿＿

　　　＿＿＿＿＿＿＿＿＿＿＿＿＿＿＿＿＿＿＿＿＿＿

网友二：你对中国文化这么了解，佩服，佩服 (pèifú, admire)！

你：　＿＿＿＿＿＿＿＿＿＿＿＿＿＿＿＿＿＿＿＿＿＿

网友二：请问你一下，听说在中国，春卷不是天天吃的东西。中国人只有在春天刚开始的时候吃春卷。这是为什么？

你：　＿＿＿＿＿＿＿＿＿＿＿＿＿＿＿＿＿＿＿＿＿＿

　　　＿＿＿＿＿＿＿＿＿＿＿＿＿＿＿＿＿＿＿＿＿＿

网友一：真是越听越想学。你知道不知道为什么中国人在过春节以前要喝一种粥，叫腊八粥？

网友二：腊八粥我喝过。

你：　＿＿＿＿＿＿＿＿＿＿＿＿＿＿＿＿＿＿＿＿＿＿

　　　＿＿＿＿＿＿＿＿＿＿＿＿＿＿＿＿＿＿＿＿＿＿

网友一：谢谢你的介绍。我想我的演讲已经准备好了。

你：　祝你好运！

VI. 小组专案活动：宣传饮食和健康 Group Project: Food and Health Education Poster

Since we discussed food and health extensively in Unit 2, let's host a food and health poster contest.

Step 1: Form groups of three or four students. Design a poster educating people about food and health. Together, you need to decide who will be in charge of each aspect of this poster production, which consists of research, design, layout, texts, printing, etc. Enter your task assignments in the form below.

宣传重点	文件	由谁负责
	上网找材料	
	设计海报	
	介绍饮食健康的文章	
	排版 (páibǎn, layout)	
	印刷 (yìnshuā, print)	

Step 2: Begin to research, draft, and create the poster according to your assignments.

Step 3: Participate in the contest: Display your poster in class and explain the poster's message to your classmates. The group that designs the most compelling poster wins the contest.